GUSTAV SCHENK

CHILTON COMPANY — BOOK DIVISION, Publishers · Philadelphia · New York

The history of man

Published simultaneously in Great Britain, America, France and Germany

Title picture: Reconstruction of a Neandertaler by J. Lukesová according to V. Fetter and M. Prokopec (Anthropological Institute of the Karls=University, Prague).

Picture 1 (Pages 2 and 3): Bas-relief from a wall of the Amon Temple at Karnak, and reconstruction of a Neandertaler according to V. Fetter and M. Prokopec.

The selection of the pictures was made by the author. — The artwork was executed by Bernd Fahrenholz, Stuttgart.
Printed in rotogravure

Fig. 2. The right hand side of the skull of Oreopithecus bambolii belonging to the complete skeleton which has been discovered (after Hürzeler).

A MAN TEN MILLION YEARS AGO?

There are great events which cannot fail to be heard and are plain to all, in the presence of which the world holds its breath. There are also others which take place circumspectly and softly but which are yet far-reaching in their effect. In 1958 and 1959 two finds of the ancestors of man of outstanding importance were made. They seem to unveil one of the greatest secrets that has occupied the attention of man for millennia: it is believed with their help to be able to come near to the solution of the riddle of the origins of man. In any event, through them the forebears of the hominines, of genuine man, have been brought within temporal striking distance.

On the 2nd August 1958 Dr. Johannes Hürzeler of Basle discovered the complete skeleton of a small-proportioned being, in a brown-coal (lignite) mine at a depth of 210 metres at Baccinello in the Italian coastal plain of Tuscany. It showed characteristics of the pongids (anthropoid apes), but also of the hominids. The stratum indicated that it had lived ten or twelve million years before in the Tertiary peat bogs of the present Tuscany. The block of brown-coal in which the fossil lay was treated with gypsum and was hewn out of the seam and brought to the surface but only with the greatest difficulty.

In the same Tuscan province of Grosseto there had already been found in 1870, also in a bed of brown-coal, a lower jaw, and it was presumed to belong to a monkey similar to the macaques owing to the peculiar structure of the molar tubercle. The fossilized remain was called Oreopithecus bambolii — monkey of Monte Bamboli after the place of discovery. In the course of about eighty years numerous fossilized fragments of the so-called hill monkey (or ape) were unearthed which without doubt belonged to the same species which had in 1958 been discovered as a complete skeleton. In 1949 Dr. Hürzeler examined the old finds most meticulously and believed that he would be able to determine their hominid nature — with the reservation, perhaps, that it was not a form which had taken a direct line towards becoming a genuine hominine (Euhominae = true men). It represented at best a highly specialized collateral branch of the Hominidae, which later, without having continued their progress, died out. Many well known investigators were of Dr. Hürzeler's opinion and added Oreopithecus to the hominid sequence. However no complete skeleton, whose discovery had long been predicted by Hürzeler, was yet forthcoming. Only with that could one hope to prove that the individual finds — several upper and lower jaw-fragments with numerous teeth — belonged to one type only. It was a veritable triumph for Hürzeler's research activities and also a most memorable occurrence for genaelogical - palaeontological research when in the summer of 1958 a complete skeleton of Oreopithecus was recovered.

Had it been "still an ape" or "already a man" a pithecus or an anthropus a pongid or an hominid? Never before had a species in the history of fossil anthropoid apes and man been fought over as was Oreopithecus. To understand the conflict of opinion, which was at bottom a fruitful and, for science, progressive discussion, the following has to be decided: since Linnaeus' "Systema Naturae", that is for 200 years, man, in spite of his special laws which separate him from all other animals, has been included in the zoological system. According to it he belongs to the Order of leading animals or Primates, which is subdivided into two suborders of the Prosimiae and the higher apes (Simiae). Three great families are included in the Simiae: the broad nosed monkey of the New World (for instance, capuchin and howler monkeys) and the narrow nosed monkeys of the Old World (for instance, baboon, mandrill or rhesus monkeys) or the man-like apes, the Hominoidea.

In this super family of Hominoidaea, anthropoid apes and man are placed together. The family includes:
1. Gibbons or hylobatids.
2. Anthropoid apes in the more restricted sense or pongids, with orang utan, gorilla and chimpanzee.
3. Men or hominids, in which true men or Homininae form a sub family.

It would be wrong to believe that the present Primates should be thought to have made all human history. But from an historical point of view forms which are now extinct are most important, that is next to the fossil hominids. Amongst other matters it is necessary to draw attention to a peculiar state of affairs: no fossil pongid is known which distinctly shows the most pronounced and outstanding peculiarity of the present anthropoid apes, namely their acrobatic specialization, with its specially developed long arms so as to be able to "brachiate" (swing from branch to branch) through the forest. The pongid as a long-armed tree-swinger and climber seems to be a very recent form of development, an adaptation to the rain forest, an over-specialization that the Oreopithecus did not yet possess. Had Oreopithecus belonged to the hominid branch, then it certainly was not yet a man in our sense, no hominine, no true man who as Homo sapiens first appeared in the last glacial period of the Ice Age.

Among the "man-like" creatures who have appeared in the course of ten million years and who now are fairly well known by reason of their fossil skeletal remains, some peculiar strange looking beings saw the light of day. Certainly they were hominid types but a tyro would never recognise them as human beings. They are called pre-hominines or pre-human. One thing however particularly distinguished them from the present pongids and simultaneously brought them near the fossil anthropoid apes: they were no brachiating long-armed climbers, no primeval forest specialists but upright-walking inhabitants of savannahs or lightly wooded tree steppes. Oreopithecus — like probably all fossil pongids and certainly like all fossil hominids — shows in his bodily structure no distinct characteristics of the brachiator, it is not therefore nearly so simple to arrive at a decision. Also there is naturally a whole series of other characteristics which separate the pongids and the hominids, for instance the morphology of the teeth. But for the Oreopithecus they did not suffice to provide an unequivocal decision from science as to its status. Much had been expected from a close scrutiny of the recovered skeleton, particularly regarding the nature of the pelvis and spinal column of the Tuscan bog-dweller. For some researchers the position was clear, for others it failed. Some voices carrying weight — Dr. Gottfried Kurth, A. H. Schultz, Professor Adolf Remane and Professor O. E. Schindewolf — declared for the absolute pongid nature of Oreopithecus.

The true importance of the discovery lies perhaps upon quite a different plane. In the lively analyses of the Oreopithecus the critical senses were sharpened. In the face of important palaeontological finds a natural impatience to reach a decision as soon as possible must be curbed. The discovery in Tuscany makes it clear to the amateur lover of science that the ontogenesis of man does not run a consistent and purposeful course. Evolution is a many-sided complex, often quite inscrutable process. No "genealogical tree" in which all is laid out graphically and logically, can help us. It is significant that a genealogical tree does not bear the slightest resemblance, even as a sketch, to a living tree with all its innumerable branches and twigs, its wavering irregularities, its interwoven net-like framework. On the enormous Tree of Life there grew up a single little twig among a thousand others, which led to anthropoid apes and man. This again consisted of a multitude of seeds, buds, shoots, leaflets, a network of pongid lines and hominid twigs of which only a few have survived. In this matted frame-work Oreopithecus may have been more progressive, more human than the near-men, half-men or apemen ten million years after him — it may just as easily be the reverse!

New discoveries can at any moment demolish a controversial, painfully obtained picture.

Oreopithecus existed when the anthropoid apes were not yet highly specialized, brachiating, long-armed climbers in their last retreat in the primeval rain forest. Man does not descend from such specialized anthropoid apes, as we now know. The

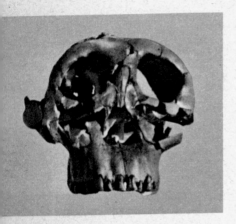

Fig. 3. The almost complete skull of Zinjanthropus boisei from the Olduvai Gorge in Tanganyika discovered by L.S.B. Leakey and his wife.

large apes of today have developed in a direction quite different to man. They cannot be our ancestors. Oreopithecus fills a palaeontological gap about ten million years ago within the history of the hominids. A further ten million years, to the beginning of the Glacial period is fossil-less insofar as the pedigree of the hominids is concerned. Thus we must gratefully welcome the appearance of the

Oreopithecus from the darkness of the brown-coal pit at Baccinello.

The second discovery which aroused enthusiasm was made exactly a year later in East Africa. The research couple Dr. L. S. B. Leakey and his wife succeeded in the summer of 1959 in recovering an almost complete skull in excellent condition from Olduvai Gorge in Northern Tanganyika Territory (already famous by their previous finds of palaeolithic cultures there). It was the skull of an Australopithecine of which hitherto about 100 individuals had been found at five different spots in South Africa. These possessed the brain of an anthropoid ape yet the cranium was ape-like and human at the same time. Body, limbs and pelvis allowed one to infer an upright carriage. In their general build they were nearer to man than to the large apes. They lived 600,000 to 400,000 years ago. The use of fire was unknown to them and, as had been believed until recently, only naturally shaped bone tools were used and they were unable to make any implements for themselves. Nevertheless the Australopithecines have been credited with quite human attributes of which man alone is capable. With the help of his creative brain he is able to make an environment, social conditions and a culture of his own. Leakey and his wife, however, found at the same time as the skull of their approximately eighteen year old Zinjanthropus boisei (Zinj is the ancient Egyptian name for East Africa and Charles Boise financed Leakey's expedition) intentionally shaped and sharpened stone implements — together with the "bag" of game. The "southern ape" or "half man" was a hominid, a pre-human who was intelligent and had foresight and could make artefacts. With the manufacture of stone implements this particular East African species of the Australopithecines had long passed over the threshold of becoming a man and had created his own culture.

The discoveries of Oreopithecus who existed about ten million years before, to the maker of implements, Zinjanthropus some 600,000 years ago, opened an unsuspected vista of the history of man.

I

THE ANCESTORS OF MAN

The highest forms of all present flora and fauna, including man, descend from forebears which were formerly more simply constructed. The forms of life then did not show such a high degree of differentation and specialization as those beings today which have a high level of organization. Since Darwin's renowned theory "The Origin of Species" modern research, one hundred years later, can form a very exact picture of the relationship of living creatures. From that one can conceive the history of life as a kind of ladder of nature. From the relatively simplest

foundation of life there has emerged the limitless and differentiated present world of organisms. The direction of development, the "trend", that is the tendency in the evolution of organisms, was not settled unequivocally. Nature did not aim directly to create out of the "incomplete" finally a "complete" creature, perhaps man. Far from striving after a single-minded development of life, nature tried the most diverse possibilities equally. She cast backward or forward and wandered into blind alleys — until at last, instead of a blind ending to a path of development, a fairly straight course, either hastened or delayed, could be held. What forces guided this ramified or criss-crossed evolution will not be discussed at this point. We have here an opportunity of surveying the picture of progressing development. Looking back from our point of view into the womb of time when life on this planet commenced, one can follow the labyrinthine road which led to us men. In the endless chain of lines of relationships leading to the erect, hairless, large brained Homo sapiens, we recognise from the alteration of attitude through which he had to pass to become as he is today, the tarsier, insectivore, marsupial, reptile, amphibian, fish, annelid, amoeba or unicellular creature and finally the first albumen jelly in the primeval ocean three thousand million years ago — these are some of the characteristic figures in the line of our forefathers.

There are two secrets which challenged the imagination and thought

A I R	Names of species (left to right)	Millions of years before the present	Duration in millions of years	World Ages
	Glowing molten mass of earth's surface	5000	2000	Pre-Genesis
	Large molecules Gelatine of albumen mucous, Bacteria	3000	1800	Lower Pre-Cambrian
	Amoebae, Volvox algae Actinotrocha, Sponges, Radiolarians			
	Seaweed, Algae-colonies, Flagellate algae			
	Sponges, Seaweed, Giant seaweed, Coral	1200	600	Upper Pre-Cambrian
	Brachiopods, Various forms of Annelidae			
	Trilobites			
	Grapholites, Corals, Sea lilies, Lancet fish, Gymnophytes, Ferns, Pewter grass (equisetum), Acanthus, Dipsacus, Psilophytes	600	100	Cambrian
	Scorpion, spider, Milliped, Equisetum			
	Ammonite, Lungfish, Crossopterygian, Amphibian, Tailed amphibian (urodeles), Tracheata	490	60	Ordovician
		430	30	Silurian

Fig. 5. Basic form of a coelomate. The coelomata are one of the main families of the metazoa which embrace everything from the annelids to the mammals. They possess a secondary body-cavity (coelom) with blood vessels (A and B), the beginning of a brain (C), mouth (D) and anus (E). The figure shows the basic type, the hypothetical ori-

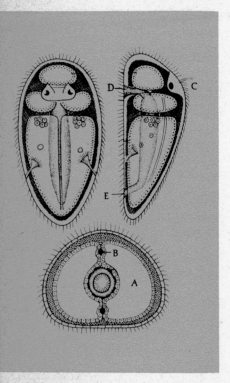

ginal-coelomata after A. Remane. From such wormlike forebears of the coelomata two phylae of animals emerged: the echinoderms and the chordata which are creatures with a back or dorsal cord. Only the chordate branch could lead to the vertebrates, fishes, amphibians, reptiles, birds and mammals. The sub-branch of echinoderms did not develop beyond the sea urchins, starfish, sea cucumbers, ophiura and their relatives.

of humanity since the most ancient times, the origin of life and the riddle of the creation of man. On the latter an uncertainly flickering light has now fallen.

The origin of life is still wrapped in darkness although numerous theories have tried to explain the inexplicable. It is possible that after the asteroid period of the earth the first organic combinations appeared as large molecules in a warm primeval ocean and at last in the form of albuminous matter and nucleic acids. From these initial steps of life the first unicellular creatures emerged two and a half thousand million years ago. In two thousand million years-old slates in Canada were found fossilized algae. The blue gelatine-like algae which are chlorophyll-containing threads of cells, could already separate, in water with the help of light, hydrogen and oxygen from each other. With the appearance of chlorophyll (the leaf green) photosynthesis became possible and through this the original food of all creatures alive, carbohydrates, could be produced. The present bacteria, amoebas and algae may serve as a sort of model of the life in the primeval ocean of the archaic world. The unicellular life there, gelatine-like dots of plasma still drifting without purpose at the mercy of all movements of the sea, did not remain undifferentiated but may well have developed cell organisms very early such as a cell "mouth" and "anus", eye patches and channels of excitation which must not on any account be called primitive. As life appeared on earth it became at once of overwhelming power and astonishing sensibility even in the seemingly poor garments of unicellularity. In spite of outward passivity it withstood mighty natural forces.

In this early age during which, after the completion of a primordial Pacific Ocean, the earliest folds of the armoured cover to our earth were executed and a second miracle of life developed: the algae formed fringes (cilliae) or whips (flagellae) by means of which they moved independently. The unicellular flagellates collected into colonies. There exist even now species of such free-swimming cell colonies; for instance the plant-like spherical volvox. Thousands of bodies and sexual cells are united in a gelatinous hollow sphere. The bodies die off after a while whereas the egg cells, fertilized mostly by spermata, the zygotes continue to reproduce themselves after the death of the mother-sphere. The path of development of life during myriads of years can be reconstructed and one can conclude from a present volvox sphere that a similar form of life existed on earth throughout the ages. It may have been the ancestral forefathers of the animal multicellular beings (metazoa) possibly first the nemato-

Fig. 6. Inhabitants of the pre-Cambrian sea: Algae, flagellate algae, volvox algae, sponges, medusae, flat worms, brachiopoda, echinoderms and molluscs. All plant and animal life was present only in the oceans; the land was "waste and void". The vertebrates also could only develop in the sea, through worms and lancet fish to real fish.

Fig. 7. The plants had first to leave the sea and conquer the unpopulated dry shores to allow the animals to follow. From mighty brown algae forests between tide marks the naked plants developed, until they became independent of the sea by means of water-carrying vessels and supporting frames, with roots and spore carriers they were able to live ashore. Primordial ferns, acanthus and pewter grass (equisetum), were the plant pioneers which made it possible for the animals to leave the seas and to instal themselves on land in a new guise.

phores and ctenophora. But only the last of the four main branches of the metazoa, the coelomata, led through worm-like early stages to the mammals. Sponges, nematophores and ctenophora have remained to this day what they were in the pre-Cambrian seas round about a thousand million years ago.

From primeval ages until the beginning of the Paleozoic era all branches of the invertebrates developed in the seas. The coelomata split up into two groups. Only the second form of coelomata (the deuterostomia) led to the vertebrates through one of the most important branches in man's history, the chordata. Chorda means sinew or chord. The chordata were creatures fitted with a dorsal chord, a cartilage-like predecessor of the spinal column. Here it is very obvious that one cannot ascribe to the much ramified development of life any striving after a particular goal, after an "upper" or "higher" target although a higher development has in fact followed. From our point of view and looking

backwards, we can survey the departed days of evolution — but at that time it was by no means to be expected (had there been a person of penetrating intelligence present) that only thus could the road be followed. Creatures capable of development, powerful groups, died out. Although they had existed for hundreds of millions of years there remained of them perhaps only one single species — but this surviving species then renewed itself in the most wonderful manner. With sudden vitality it cast off its ancient covering and slipped into a new form. There were also possibilities which were not used. So the "construction plans" fluctuated between the invertebrates and the vertebrates; they were in fact not planned. Only

from our point of view does it seem as if life had been arranged from the beginning for the perfection of the chordata.

Modern evolutionary research can today separate the invertebrates less easily from the vertebrates than could be done before. The marine tunicates and salps are closely related to the vertebrates, indeed they are the descendants of the vertebrate's oldest ancestors. The still living acrania presumably dug itself into the sands on seashores in Ordovician or Silurian times some 500 million years ago and stirred up its pond with its ciliae. It lacks a head and is brainless but possesses an elastic backbone — a chorda dorsalis, a dorsal marrow with light-sensitive cells, a vascular system and a heart of contractive tubular segments. Only from living types like the living lancetfish or acrania could the true vertebrates first as fishes unfold, with their special characteristics such as their many-layered outer skin (epidermis), with a five lobed brain, eyes which grew out of the inner-brain, a branchial intestine, thyroid glands, liver and heart and blood vessels. Jaw-less agnatha which were similar to our remora and lampreys, represented the first stage of vertebrates. To them belonged also the ostracodermata, amongst which was a species whose forepart was enclosed in a skin of armour whilst the body was protected by bony skin or a carapace.

Later jaw-bearing armoured fish occurred whose chief group was represented by the placodermata. Their foreparts were enclosed in a capsule of bony skin and the head armour was divided from a body armour which was in the shape of a shoulder girdle. The armoured fishes did not belong to a fixed type; their adventurous body-forms were extraordinarily rich in numbers and specifically adapted to their diverse surroundings, mostly inland waters.

From the ancient ostracodermata were developed the bony fish (osteichtyes) with their thin skinned fins. Fin muscles and fin skeleton had retrogressed and thus came about the actinopterigii with their great mobility. They comprise today over 30,000 species, 95% of the present fishes. Immediately on their appearance in the Devonian Era the ray-fins separated into lungfish (dipnoi) and crossopterygii. The lungfish, with lung and gill breathing, dug themselves into the ooze when the waters they inhabited dried and survived the drought in a summer sleep. The tassel-fins, also breathing with a swim-bladder lung, could travel overland during dry periods to seek new waters. The muscular fringed fins of the tassel-fins were so articulated with the body that they possessed very wide possibilities of movement. Their lung, richly supplied with blood through capillary vessels, approached that of the future land vertebrates much more nearly than the lung of the dipnoi.

A specialized collateral branch of the tassel-fins, the coelacanthidae, later visited the open oceans, lost

Fig. 8. The lancet fish (A), which even now can be found buried in the sand in shallow parts, for instance, of the North Sea, possesses no skull and no brain. It serves as a model of a connecting link between the invertebrates and the vertebrates. Beside a spinal cord with light-sensitive cells it is also furnished with an elastic spinal rod.

Our present lamprey (B) stands close to the lancet fish yet it is more highly organised. The first skull had been created with a simple brain protected by cartilaginous plates.

The lung fishes (C) of the Devonian were dipnoans which had besides their gills a swimbladder lung. In the event of its habitat drying it dug itself into the mud and survived the drought in a summer sleep.

The crossopterygians (D) also breathe like the lung fish, and by means of their wide tassel-like muscular fins go overland in order to seek new waters during dry periods. A branch of these crossopterygians became the ancestors of the original amphibian the true quadruped leading an amphibious life.

A

B

C

D

AIR	Names of species (left to right)	Millions of years before the present	Duration in millions of years	World Ages
	Sharks Ichtyostega (fins turned into limbs)	400	50	Devonian
	Sharks Lepidodendreae Stegocephales, giant forms of pewter grass Dragonfly	350	70	Carboniferous
	Archelon (Giant turtle) Edaphosaurus, Cygnognathus (mammal like) Dragonfly	270	50	Permian
	Elasmosaurus, Turtle, Plateosaurus, Duckbill, Saltoposuchus	220	40	Triassic
	Ichtyosaurus, Crab Camptosaurus, Compsognathus, Allosaurus, Gymnosperms Flying saurians, Archeopterix, Butterfly	180	45	Jurassic
	Sawfish, Tylosaurus Elasmosaurus, Thylacodon (predecessor of the Kangaroo rat), Brontosaurus, Tyrannosaurus, Fan palm, Flying saurians. Butterfly	135	65	Cretaceous

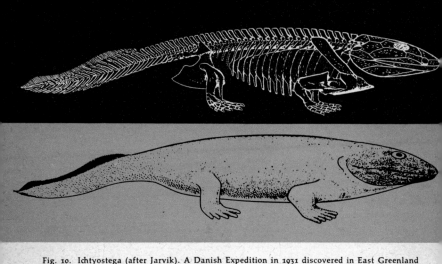

Fig. 10. Ichtyostega (after Jarvik). A Danish Expedition in 1931 discovered in East Greenland the fossil which caused such a stir. In the Devonian of 400 m.y. ago this transitional form already lived, between fish and amphibian and very similar to the tassel-fin crossopterygian.

The four footed primordial amphibian with its fishes' tail could traverse bogs and mudbanks by means of its fin-like legs. It was a clumsy, ungainly animals with pendent belly and weak feet which could only be moved with the help of the body in a kind of "shove run". The fossil discovery of the hitherto oldest land vertebrate confirmed the great value of palaeontology. In East Greenland there had been found an unexpected "missing link" between fish and amphibian. With the primordial amphibian, which could reach a length of 1 m, commenced the period of the conquest of terra firma by the tetrapoda.

their swimbladder lung and breathed like all fish only by means of gills, and still live as several species in tropical seas. Only one strain of tassel-fins which preserved its originality became the ancestors of all terrestrial vertebrates. Two stocks of this strain were clearly characterised by fourfootedness (tetrapody) and also showed the shadowy appearance of a fivefingered hand. One tassel-fin family led to the present tailed amphibians (urodeles) the newts and salamanders, and the other to the tail-less amphibians (anures). From the urodeles, reptiles and mammals would develop. In the thirties of this century — when a recent species of the primeval tassel-fin which had been thought long since extinct was found living in the Indian Ocean — a Danish expedition to East Greenland found the fossilized remains of an original amphibian with a fishes' tail. This ichthyostega which resembled a tassel-fin in many respects, even if with more powerful limbs, was a genuine quadruped with two pairs of legs, whose propagation, like all amphibians', remained bound to the water. In the larval stage it had only pure gill breathing. In steamy, well watered, swampy lands it moved about with a pendulous belly, more crawling and creeping than walking. It led the way for the amphi-

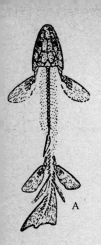

Fig. 11. The arising of reptiles out of fish and through amphibians (after O. Kuhn) (A) a fish from the Devonian, (B) an amphibian from the Carboniferous, (C) a primeval reptile from the Permian. This comparison, which is supported by numerous palaeontological finds, makes the course of an advancing development, an evolution of the organism, peculiarly clear. In the course of 160 m.y., fish and reptile had been transformed to a being which had been made completely independent of the sea and had become a relatively complete land animal. The larval state with gill beathing could be abandoned and the stiffshelled eggs could be laid on land.

bians of the stegocephales groups whose skull roof was still closed and whose break-through in the region of the temples had not yet appeared. When the amphibians also had become comparatively independent of the water up to the larval stage, conditions of a life ashore demanded a more powerful sense of sight and thus an enlargement of the brain and with it that of the skull, as well as greater activity through more lively movements which could only be brought about by a higher development of the extremities. In the terrestrial reptiles which emerged from the amphibians, the skull became domed, the closed skull roof was pierced by windows, the brain could expand, the limbs became more mobile and — the most significant alteration of all — the reptiles laid their hard-shelled eggs on land. The larval stage with gill-breathing was replaced by hatching the fully developed, lungbreathing young.

The reptile could go wherever it liked and dominate the continents. Beside the collateral branches of new forms of life the old original stocks, like amphibians and reptiles, were conserved to our times. Palaeontology often is confronted by large gaps in the smooth course of the development of animals. These do not mean that there are natural breaks

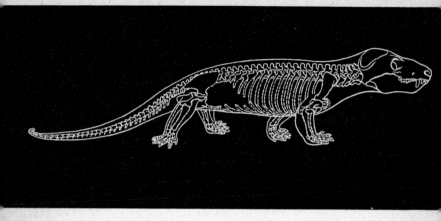

Fig. 12. Among the land inhabiting reptiles of the Permian and of the Triassic some 250 m.y. ago there were a special group which already presented the peculiar characteristics of mammals. This Cynognathus (after Gregory and Camp) with its slender predatory-mammal form and dentition which was differentiated by gripping teeth (incisors), catching teeth (canines) and grinding teeth (molars). The mammal aspect was here pre-empted, for Cynognathus possessed a pronounced reptile-like brain. It is possible that it even produced living young (viviparous). It belongs to the Therapsid Order amongst the reptiles. Many species of them show mammal characteristics. In the trough of the Basin of the Karroo in South Africa, 1300 km long and 530 km broad, there have hitherto been found 350 species of such flesh and insect eating, mobile reptiles with mammal-like bodies and the extended skull forms of predators. A sedimentary layer in the Basin has even been called the Cynognathus Zone after the numerous finds.

in evolution. The absence of fossil information merely gives an appearance of a development of life by jumps. Darwin also complained of the incompleteness of the palaeontological record. But after him palaeontology developed spectacularly. Such finds as that of Ichthyostega in

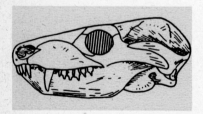

Greenland show very clearly that types of living creatures do not proceed without transition in stages or in jumps. Whole armies of researchers are busy every day all over the world trying to find ever more material confirming their view, that life develops on an evenly ascending plane and not in steplike stages. The fish-amphibian from Greenland represents one of the many triumphs of palaeontology. It makes it easy to understand that fishes and amphibians must have advanced in a smoothly progressing development which lasted many million years, leading to the reptiles.

Fig. 13. The duckbill which inhabits Australia is a model of the primordial mammal. Like a reptile it lays hard-shelled eggs, it hatches them out, however, in a nest chamber and feeds the young from the breast but not by means of mammae but through sieve-like parts of the skin. The duckbill is still almost in the act of metamorphosis.

The reptiles from the Permian period replaced the damp-loving amphibians comparatively rapidly and developed tremendously in the more open country resulting from a cooler and dryer climate. Savannahs, steppes, desert steppes, and genuine deserts hemmed in the damp and hot primeval forests and jungles of the Carboniferous period more and more. The hothouse atmosphere of the world became a rough and hard place. The steppes of the Permian period brought the "amniotic groups", land creatures with a water filled eggshell (amnion).

From amphibians with domed skulls, from lizard-like, crocodile-

Fig. 14. Two skulls of mammal-like reptiles of the Order of Therapside.
They derive from the Triassic 240 m. y. ago and belonged to creatures of cat-like or dog-like figure. These carnivores appeared shortly before the mammals. Of a certain species one may even assume that they were covered in a mammal-like skin; the pits in their skulls even seem to indicate whiskers and, based on the form of the pelvis one may assume them to have been vivi-parous. Palaeontology is of the opinion that the genealogical history of mammals has its roots in the Therapsids. Such fossil dis-coveries are of high value; the preparation for a quite new type of creature is seen in them.

Fig. 15. Archaeopterix (primordial bird). The bird's feathers arose from the scales of the reptiles. The primordial birds were preceded by the warm-blooded flying lizards with the characteristics of true reptiles. The archaic bird also, with its clawed fingers, the dentated jaws and the reptilian tail had still the characters of a saurian and yet was a true bird.

Fig. 16 (reading from the top). Compsognathus, from the family of Saurischians. It was an exceedingly swiftmoving, rapacious lizard of cat size. From such small meat-eaters or egg-stealing reptiles there developed within 180 m. y. the frightful gigantic saurians, the dimwitted murderers with the brain of a hen, for instance, the Allosaurus and the Tyrannosaurus.

Camptosaurus from the group of lizards "with the pelvis of a bird" (Ornithischians). It was a comparatively large herbivore with flat very blunt teeth in a bird-like beak. Yet beside the gigantic mountains of flesh of its relations it must have seemed tiny. Camptosaurus grazed in fertile lands, under tree ferns, pines and auracarias — but it had terrible and irresistible enemies: the predatory dinosaurs.

The most extreme predatory dinosaur of the Cretaceous 120 m. y. ago was the tyrannosaurus, a colossus of a height of more than ten metres and a total length of fifteen metres. The one metre deep mouth was studded with twenty centimetre long daggerlike teeth and the feet on his muscular hind legs ended in fearful talons. Such grotesque monsters from the Jurassic and Cretaceous epochs ruled the entire world. They had no enemies which were superior to them in strength. They rent and devoured whatever living beings they could find and which were unable to escape. Their sudden cessation 75 m. y. ago is mysterious and there are many contradictory theories to explain their disappearance. Only after their extinction was it possible for the mammals to unfold their full powers.

Fig. 17
Table III.

Development of Life in the Tertiary Period.

WATER

LAND

No reconstruction of the outward appearence of Oreopithecus is in existence, see picture of his skeleton on p. 46

AIR	Names of species (left to right)	Millions of years before the present	Duration in millions of years	World Ages
	Present fishes Plesiadis Planetetherium (Glider)	70	15	Paleocene
	Whales Tetonius, Notharctus Dragonfly, Butterfly	55	20	Eocene
	Giant vulture	35	15	Oligocene
	Proconsul Butterfly			Lower Miocene
	Dryopithecus Dragonfly	23	12	Middle Miocene
	Seals Oreopithecus Butterfly			Upper Miocene
	Seals Teatornis			Up to middle Pliocene
	Present fishes	12	11	Upper Pliocene
	Australopithecus	1	1	Pleistocene

like and newt-like animals there unfolded the original creeping animals, reptiles whose pierced temporal cavities allowed the introduction of a powerful chewing musculature. In addition 'liquor amnii' filled the eggshells and so released them completely from the need of water. Only with this land-bound line of life was the way to the birds and mammals, and thereby also to man, entered upon.

A cool dry period allowed the amphibians to become lizards. In a world climate which again became warmer and more humid, the reptiles unfolded to unprecedented numbers and varieties. Among them were the biggest predators and herbivores living on the land, monstrous lumps of flesh weighing tons. Amongst these titans, were the thirty-ton herbivorous Brontosaurus or the thirty metre long duckbilled sauropod

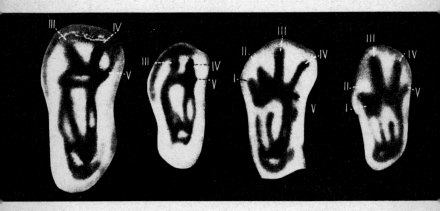

Fig. 18. The three fingered hand of a bird corresponds to our five fingered one. In the embryonal development of an ostrich's hand and foot and of that of a domestic fowl it can be seen that the first and fifth fingers have degenerated. The original bird already had this regression. It had derived from the equally retrogressed hand of the reptilian Compsognathus. From left to right: Section through the foot of a 9 day old embryo of the African ostrich. III—V the three last toe layouts, which first become visible. Section through the hand of a ten day old ostrich embryo, III—V the three last finger layouts of which those of the 5th finger did not further develop. Section through the foot of a five day 14 hours old chicken. Section through the hand of a five day ten hours

old embryo of a chicken. It can be seen clearly that fingers II, III und IV are most developed. They became the 3 fingered birdhand (after N. Holmgren).

The wings of birds are the same as the fore limbs of all higher vertebrates, and also as the human arm. The correspondences of the bird's wing to our fore arm and ulna and radius are easily found, not, however, those parts in the bird which correspond to our hand. The three fingered bird-hand has materially transformed itself. The Archaeornis and even Compsognathus, the small predacious reptile with his leaping-legs and tiny fore arms show the remarkable structure of the 1st and 2nd fingers.

with its "dental battery" of several hundred teeth arranged in three rows. Finally there was the murderous robber dinosaur, the tyrannosaurus.

To make intelligible the way of life of the animals on the mainlands and also the appearance of the first mammals, still in the shadow of the dinosaurs, we must summarise briefly. The picture of the earth often altered fundamentaly, the climate changed, and the living spaces for plant life and animals were constantly changing shape. Many creatures adapted themselves largely to the new conditions, they specialized and remained constant in their specialization as long as the habitat to which they had adapted themselves remained the same — often for hundreds of millions of years. Some species adapted themselves to the new environment but remained primitive and it was precisely these undeveloped branches which brought forth new forms which even more completely adapted themselves to new climates and wholly different environments. Should the picture change again they may die out. The survivors will again be simple unspecialized types of life. Through them evolution advances. "There are always branches capable of adaptation, which survive. Capacity for adaptation belongs however only to that which has *not yet been adapted*. For adapted means: to become unilateral . . . . specialization means a blind alley; the future belongs to 'primitiveness'" (von Bülow).

The mammals as a new type were still scarce 240 million years ago and were the size of rats and mice. In Mongolia under the eggs of dinosaurs seven small bones of a mouse-sized mammal were found from the Triassic period, and in several countries, small multicusped teeth, small jaw bones and skull remains were dug up which were identified as the remains of marsupials. Ninety million years passed after the mysterious extinction of the saurians, until highly differentiated mammals could emerge without danger into the freedom of a world evacuated by the "dragons". After a long time of development the mammal was distinguished by the following characteristics: Increase of bodily and brain size, warm-bloodedness, a highly developed dentition, forming of nose and ears, diaphragm breathing, retention of ova in the mother's womb, viviparity, perfecting of milk glands and finally the presence of a uterus and uterus-placenta for the nourishment of the embryo. The road towards this end led through animals, similar to our duck-billed platypus, to the marsupials which no longer laid eggs but gave birth to living but still very incomplete young which were suckled in a brood-sac and carried by the mother until self-sufficient. Finally the higher orders of the placentalia emerged, including the insectivores, ancestors of our hedgehogs, shrews and moles, which feed the embryo on the mother's blood.

Constant body temperature made these animals independent of their surroundings. The intensive metabolism required a perfect dentition, the special teeth required a special skull—and snout—form. The liveborn young were no longer left to chance as the oviparous reptile young were; they needed motherly care and learned by the experience of their parents which they remembered — the prosencephalon (forebrain) had to develop to an extraordinary degree.

From the end of the Cretaceous period to the beginning of the early Tertiary period lies the median zone of development which intervened between the Insectivores and the Primates. A remainder group from this zone has been preserved until today. These are the tree-shrews of the Indo-Malay region. Although they show a near relationship to the Primate group today they are classed with the Insectivores.

In the first step of the Tertiary period in the Palaeocene epoch about 75 million years ago, a plethora of Primate species appeared. There were lemurs, lorises and relations of the tarsiers which still live in the Philippines and some Indonesian islands. One can imagine them as long tailed, thickly haired nocturnal and dusk animals. Some still very primitive forms, for instance the Notharctus, we know very precisely from palaeontological finds. In the Eocene epoch 60 million years ago of the Tertiary period it was above all the ancestral forms of the tarsiers which led to the higher apes. At that time there was a great wealth of species of tarsiers. Even though of them only the Tarsius has survived to the present day, we can read the fate of

humanity from the original form of this little beast. It is quite possible to compare the survivors with their ancestors. This borderline form between lowly insect-eating mammals and the higher apes and man-like forms, was the first to find it possible with his forward directed eyes to achieve a unified sight range and to be sensible of the picture of its nocturnal jungle stereoscopically. These alert, large, apparently sad eyes of the tarsier, behind which shines a quick intelligence, still point today to the future man when one compares the survivor with his ancestor. But also another just as shattering a characteristic appears in the erstwhile Prosimiae of the Eocene epoch, which surely must have been an epoch of the "Goddess of the Dawn" (Aurora): the hand which seems to anticipate the human tool hand which later became free. And behind this hand and those eyes there are peculiarities in the perfecting of the brain which shifts it very near towards us and the anthropoid apes.

Science which concerns itself with the history of animals is not very convinced of the "higher form" of the Primates which we place at the head of the mammals. Only in the build of the brain and in its per-

Fig. 19. The Tarsius (Tarsius tarsius) the "spectral" animal of the Sunda Islands. It survived, as the sole species, its numerous ancestral forms in the early Tertiary 60 m. y. ago, from which the higher apes and man may be derived. With its forward-looking eyes it gained not only unified vision but stereoscopic sight.

formance have they reached a peak; in the form of the limbs or the teeth they have remained primitive placentalia which follow immediately upon the Insectivores (Remane). This may show the capacity of the order for adaptation which leads from relatives of Tarsius to the still "primitive" genus Homo, outside the presently living, highly specialized, unilaterally adapted anthropoid apes.

Before further following the path of becoming a man it is necessary to know what, in fact, a man is and in what respect he differs from the beasts. This seems simple, because for that purpose we need only compare ourselves with the higher animals. This is not to say that it will succeed without detailed knowledge of very involved individual detail which distinguishes itself sharply from the beast. One can say in anticipation that man's path of development diverged from all other living creatures comparitively late, namely in the Tertiary period, after the appearance of the lemurs. He separated from an animal root from which the anthropoid apes also originate, which in no sense means that man descends from

Fig. 20. The hand of a lemur, the aye-aye or finger animal, from Madagascar. A nocturnal animal of a length of some half a metre, with red-grayish hair and a bushy tail. In bamboo forests insects are its prey and with its fingers, which have claws as well as flat nails, it digs out the pith from bamboos and sugar canes. This expressive hand with its nearly equally long fingers which are unspecialized reminds one of a human hand and is very near to the hand of primitive original vertebrates.

apes as they are known to us in their present form.

Man has developed in the course of several hundred thousand years, not with a constant aim but by a selection of manifold coincidental inherited mutations. They split into many species, of which some died out. Others, however, propagated their particular characteristics in new groups of men with quite specific corporal characteristics and they, in turn, formed a network or bunch of branches of more or less related stocks. The records, as provided by the fossil history of the hominids, are not very rich — the gaps in the evidence are great—they do however confirm the fact that the hominids in the course of their long history covering millions of years have differentiated considerably in their bodily form and functions. Never in the development of the hominids has there been a creature of whom one could have said positively "a man". Recent man belongs to a unified, fixed type Homo sapiens, who is classed in the sub-family of the true men, the Homininae. He developed slowly through a series of forms which affect us nowadays as peculiar, strange and frightening. Never was there among them "the man", always there were entire groups of man-like beings who together make up the subfamily of pre-men or pre-Homininae. Among each other they were separated by as many fundamental group characteristics as present man is separated from any one of them. "Modern" man can be distinguished without trouble from the present large apes and from the

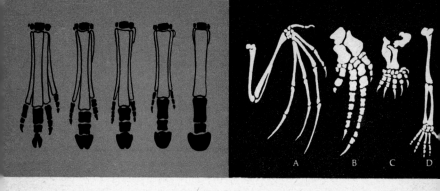

Fig. 21. Palaeontology investigates fossil documents which support the history of life upon earth. The picture on the left gives a show piece of palaeontological original information: the development of the forefoot of the horse. The fossil genealogical material of the horse-like and the horse is almost without any gaps. They developed in the Tertiary in the New World from dogsized creatures to the true horses of our day. With the growth in size of the entire animal the lateral toes regressed whilst the third toe became a hoof. It has also been attempted to determine — through anatomical comparisons of present creatures — the transitional forms which led from beast to man. The left illustration shows the skeleton of the hands of various mammals A) bat, B) whale, C) mole, D) man, (redrawn after Weinert). These are ontogenetical original information in which, as in a model, the ancestral lineage is replaced by anatomical sequence.

original apes of a million years ago. The representatives of the human group which preceded today's man are often difficult to recognise as human beings yet they belonged to the Homininae group, or true men.

There is yet another consideration which makes it difficult to discriminate between man and the nearest Primate to him: it was not alone his physical nature which in the earliest days distinguished man to a greater or lesser extent from the beasts and which today so clearly divides him from them. The biological-scientific picture of man is not enough to be able to say: what is man? and in what respect is he different from other beings? A natural history of man which describes the creation and development of the human species,

can only define man since the circumstances of his being have differed fundamentally from all other living creatures. His spirit is capable of pondering on himself and on the world. He can decide freely to name things with his gift of speech and to remove from them to a distance. With freedom of choice, with the world at his disposal thought, language, spirit and belief, the gift, of sensibility and civilization, he has become a rare phenomenon amongst the animals. He has built himself surroundings with his sociological order and his culture which is removed completely from a conformity to natural biological law.

All this cannot be seen from the recovered fossil skeletal remains. The centre of gravity of the human spe-

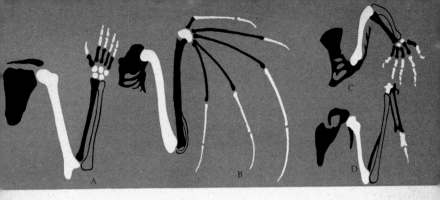

Fig. 22. In this illustration also valuable proofs of the evolution of organisms are presented — again based on comparative anatomy. Here the same bones from the arm of A) a man, B) a bat, C) a lizard and D) an eagle are given the same colour. They show the common structural plan in these four descendants of the reptiles (redrawn after J. Huxley).

cies lies in their spiritual behaviour and in their culture. Thus, after reaching the animal-man field of transition, after overcoming the sub-human and still bestial phase (G. Heberer) the cultures have almost vanished without trace since arte-facts were only in the rarest instances of stone or were capable of fossili-zation; that is to say they consisted of clothing, wood and thatched huts, wooden idols, wooden utensils or reed mats, animal skins and hair. Only burial grounds, appearing very late, and the rock paintings are im-portant indications pointing to the spiritual and sociological side of primeval man.

To be able to assign correctly men and beasts to their correct species one must not imagine the higher ani-mals as being too human or use ex-cessive imagination regarding the special place of man with relation to natural laws. Since it is, from a biological point of view, impossible to have an unadapted being, even man must also not, as one theory asserts, be regarded as a deficient being. The deficiency is said to show itself in that man lacks essential spe-cial adaptations and is compelled hence to provide himself with tools, weapons and clothing. The human brain, with its immense size, implies a very special adaptation. Besides, the specialization of man lies precisely in that he is not adapted one-sidedly; his many-sidedness and versatility and his spectacular eagerness for novelty and the unknown has preser-ved his inquisitiveness (C. K. Lorenz). According to Lorenz, there are three prerequisites which allowed man to arrive: his broadmindedness, his curiously inquisitive behaviour and his self-domestication.

These views help us further only on condition that we assess the fossil record. To be able to state: this bone

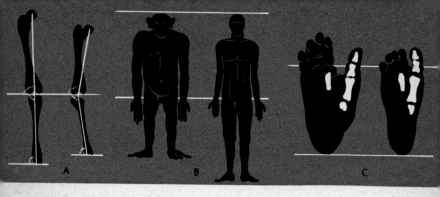

Fig. 23. This picture is intended to show how the human leg and foot are distinct from those of an anthropoid ape: the erect carriage characterises the human body. As compared with the anthropoid apes man has the longer legs. Exceedingly powerful leg muscles attached to equally strong longitudinal bones stretch the body, keep it upright and support a bumpy up and down walk. Only man possesses nates (buttocks) and calves. The hind limbs of the anthropoid apes have in man become a vertical pillar. The foot as a platform (A) vertical axis of leg in man and gorilla (redrawn after Weidenreich). (B) relative length of leg in chimpanzee and man (redrawn after A. H. Schultz). (C) foot of chimpanzee and man (redrawn after A. H. Schultz).

Fig. 24. Comparison between the foot of man and of chimpanzee. The unilateral adaptation of the chimpanzee to the primeval forest as a brachiator shows not only in the arms which, as distinct from ours, are greatly lengthened but also the gripping feet in which the opposable thumbs are one-sidedly developed. The legs are shorter than the arms and the thumbs are comparitively weakly developed.

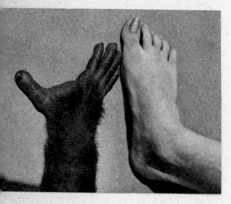

fragment belonged to a being who was "still-a-monkey" (pithecus) and that skeleton to "already-a-man" (anthropus), one must rely on few and purely anatomical characteristics which show this clearly. There are therefore only the fundamental, the most important distinguishing characteristics which differentiate man from man-ape:

1. Upright bearing and erect carriage.
2. The pliable spinal column carries the head on a stalk-like neck and cushions the bumpy upright walk.
3. Pelvis and chest-cavity become wider and shallower, the spatulas shift backwards.
4. The very long columnar legs have exceedingly powerful muscles.

5. The heelbone (os calcis) of the foot grows in size. The wide and flat big toe which lies against the other toes characterises the typical human foot which must carry the upright walking Primate.

6. By adopting an erect stance the arms and their hands are freed and no longer used to serve progression. Only after upright carriage had been achieved could the hand become a very pronounced human tool hand. Only now could the sub-human phase be overcome and the human hominid become a "tool maker".

7. The hands grasp, hold tight, tear and divide what once the snout did. Snout and canine teeth become involuted. In the human

Fig. 25. Comparison between the hand in man and chimpanzee. The thumbs of the chimpanzee hand are developed only weakly; the chimpanzee hand is no tool-hand as in man.

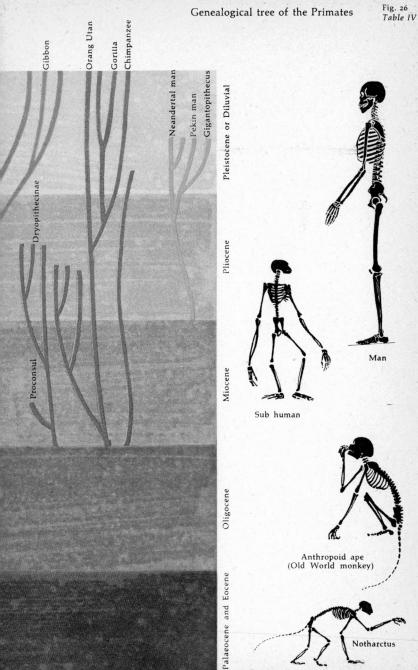

Genealogical tree of the Primates

Fig. 26
Table IV

Gibbon

Orang Utan

Gorilla

Chimpanzee

Neandertal man

Pekin man

Gigantopithecus

Dryopithecinae

Proconsul

Pleistocene or Diluvial

Pliocene

Miocene

Oligocene

Palaeocene and Eocene

Man

Sub human

Anthropoid ape
(Old World monkey)

Notharctus

Fig. 27. Specifically human characters show in a pronounced manner in a comparison of the size and erectness of the other Primates, as shown in the illustration. From left to right: tree-shrew, lemur, cercopithecus a gorilla who is supported on his hands and a gorilla who is standing erect, and man. The upright carriage and the capacity of his brain raises man above all other animals. In addition, there is the great use he makes of the senses, ears and eyes, which are focussed on the distance. The sense of smell, which in low-slung animals is especially developed, is, on the other hand, less developed (redrawn after Portmann and v. Eickstedt).

hand the free movement of the index finger shows a very characteristic human trait; the index finger is, after Wood-Jones, the most human of all fingers.

8. Only after standing up could the distant senses of sight and hearing, contrary to the near sense of smell, develop powerfully.

9. Simultaneously with the mighty increase in the volume of the brain was the hand, face, hearing, spiritual bearing and finally speech developed.

10. The cranium has been raised and domed beyond all animal measure. In contradistinction to the forehead retreating flat to the rear in the higher apes with their frontal superciliary arch and bony prominence, the human brow rises steeply and high.

11. The muscle-bound apish skull, which is still often furnished with a cranial crest to support the masseter muscles, disappears in man at once on the involution of the cervical muscles. In spite of the gracility, the refinement and diminution of the human face, the facial muscles are enriched. They offer man the possibility of giving play to his feeling in many ways.

12. With the involution of the snout to a mouth, the seam of the mouth also is curled over and becomes a lip which not only picks up food but also masters speech.

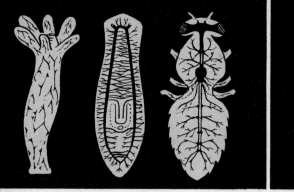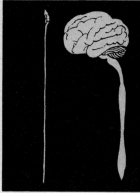

Fig. 28. The centralisation of the nervous system was a prerequisite to becoming human. In the picture from left to right: the nerve complex of a freshwater polyp is still diffuse and uncultivated. The turbellaria worm shows a first bundle of nerves, whilst in the bee the bundles of nerves strengthened and a kind of brain developed as a sensory centre at the end of the head. The two drawings on the extreme right reproduce only the brain and spinal cord of a fish and man, reduced to the same length (after Schwidetzky).

13. Man is born naked like the anthropoids, but he remains naked whilst the great apes grow a coat of hair as they get older. Man never reaches, with his poverty of hair, the stage of hairiness of the man-apes.

"Man is a sexually matured Primate embryo" was the startling general conclusions of science. Another characteristic of the "infantility" and "primitiveness" of man is, of course, his hand which with its almost equally long fingers has been left behind ontogenetically and remains un-specialized. Yet in spite of this the index finger became moveable in such a typically human manner and the simple unadapted hand became a tool-hand, which surpasses the hands of all animals. Intentionally, only the bodily characteristics of

man have here been submitted in order to be able to appreciate properly the fossil records of the lemuroid, primitive apes and great apes and the skeletal remains of early man. On the physical side the differences between the higher animals and man are not nearly so great, and some characteristics in fact bear witness that man has in certain respects remained simple and primitive. Even in his high differentation of the brain (cerebralization) he has not achieved a one-sided adaptation. This "braining" first developed after the achievement of an upright carriage. In all vertebrates a new anatomical type is always preceded by brain development. Yet with erection already present, and with a still moderate volume of brain, man became divorced from animals. From the point of view of the anatomy the differences between the lowest and the highest Primates are only differences of degree of a mixed kind, not in a difference of importance or value. In physiological functions for instance, the chimpanzee is quite equal to man. In his bodily characteristics man is indissolubly included in the intertwining chain of the tangled animal world. He belongs to the sweeping ascending evolution which is most wonderfully shown in zoology. In his bodily build man possesses nothing which has not slowly developed in the correct sequence. This sequence was laid down in the first bundle of nerves in the worm, in the sensory centre of the insects and lastly in the brain and spinal cord of fishes and reptiles. But under the guidance of his creative brain, through his spiritually

conducted dealing and the understanding of his acts, man created with his tradition a new sort of "heritage". This made culture possible. Apart from cultural and sociological beginnings in early days, this belongs to a different history of man, the cultural and spiritual history.

Armed with this more profound intelligence one can again turn to the fossil records which lead to man. The fossil history of the apes is very incomplete. Science can now, with numerous discoveries available, establish an ontogenetical connection between tarsiers, lemuroids and the first true anthropoid apes. The skull of a tarsius-like creature in Wyoming, the very small Tetonius homunculus, bridges the gap between the insectivorous nocturnal forest Primates the Prosimiae and the man-like apes. Besides Notharctus (see p. 32) and Tetonius, there is yet one find from Buchsweiler in Lower Alsace which Dr. Hürzeler described. The teeth of the tarsius-like Alsaticopithecus represent the oldest of the

Fig. 29. This lower jaw is 40 m. y. old from the Oligocene epoch of the Tertiary period. It was found in the fertile oasis of El Fayum south-westward of Cairo where many Tertiary mammals, also primates were dug up. This discovery has great importance ontogenetically. Propliopithecus haeckeli the creature was called from which the jaw originates (after Schlosser).

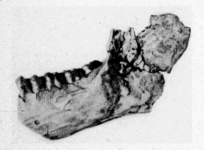

Fig. 30. 25 m. y. ago there lived in thinly wooded country or on wooded steppes in East Africa, Proconsul, a primordial anthropoid ape. It was distinguished (like man) from the present anthropoid apes by the absence of the large incisors and the simian shelf, a thickening on the inner side of the lower jaw bone. It also did not possess the apish heavy brow ridges. Of all anthropoid apes the Proconsul-like creatures were the most likely from which a human development could proceed. They are to a certain extent a model for the derivation of the family history from brachiating anthropoid apes on one hand and the upright walking man on the other, from earlier types (after Oakley and Wilson). ▷

man-likes apes, the 40 million year old Parapithecus ("near ape", for perhaps he was not a Primate at all.) Its lower jaw was found in a sacred area of Upper Egypt in the El Fayum Oasis. A primitive ape from the "Sealand" depression in the Libyan desert also showed tarsioid features. Again a brighter light was shed from El Fayum on the history of the apes and hence also on the history of man. It was there that these remains of the lower jaws of a primeval man-ape, the Propliopithecus haeckeli, were discovered. Beside it the Parapithecus seems so primitive that it might even have come from the Eocene epoch some 20 million years older. Through Le Gros Clark and L. S. B. Leaky the Propliopithecus haeckeli acquired another ancestor some 10 million years more recent, the Limnopithecus from the Miocene epoch in Kenya, East Africa. He was without any doubt whatever already a true anthropoid ape and an original ancestor of all the gibbons.

Although the present gibbons have brought brachiation — as a special adaptation to the rain forest — to a fine art, the original gibbon did not yet posses this one-sided specialization, although they could "practise" it. This adaptation to the primeval rain forest, by which the gibbon of the present swings amongst the trees with the ease of a ballet dancer and the grace of an acrobat, was developed very late historically — much too late to be regarded as a preliminary step to erect carriage (G. Heberer).

Ernst Haeckel had in 1896 already enunciated the hypothesis that a gibbon ancestor had been the forefather of the present man-apes. Modern research agreed with him in certain respects. The two genera Propliopithecus and Limnopithecus are so closely related that they can be included in one group. In such a group lies the root from which the man-apes grew.

During the very long period of the Miocene which began 30 million years ago and lasted 20 million years, there were distributed in Equatorial Africa, in Europe, India and China true man-apes in the most diverse

Fig. 31. The skeleton of Oreopithecus bambolii. Here shown prepared on one side only having been removed from a block of brown-coal. In August 1958 Dr. Hürzeler of Basle was able to recover the complete skeleton of, in his opinion, a possible hominid creature. It was found 210 m. below the surface in a brown-coal pit at Bacinello in the Province of Grosseto in Italy. It lived some 10 m. y. ago in the bog forests of the present Tuscany. Oreopithecus, after the form of the molar teeth cusps, was the name given in 1870 by researchers to the supposed cercopithecus of which they had found fragments of dentition and jaws. Hürzeler had since 1949 examined the old discoveries and believed he recognised the hominid nature of the fossils.

Fig. 32. Could Oreopithecus in Tuscany have been an ape or almost a man already — he lived in subtropical tree bogs. Ferns, reeds, palms, poplars and swamp cypress surrounded him.   ▷

Fig. 33. Proconsul inhabited a savannah region but also tree steppes, well grassed plains dotted with isolated clumps of trees. Only in such environments could the upright bearing of the hominids be attained.   ▷

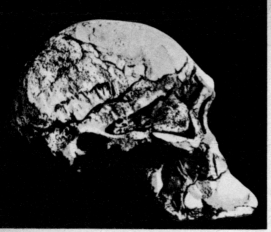

Fig. 34. The illustration shows the best preserved skull of a "Southern ape" or Australopithecus (after Knussmann). This form among the whole group was called Plesianthropus (= near man). At five different sites the remains of over 100 individuals of Australopithecus have been hitherto found; they lived half a million years ago and probably preserved themselves as a group until 300,000 to 400,000 years ago. It is not clear whether these living beings with the brain of a man-ape and the erect posture of a man were still apes (pithecus) or were already human (anthropus), still animals (subhuman) or already human.

Fig. 35. In 1938 near Sterkfonteyn in South Africa another form, the Paranthropus (near man or beyond him) was found clearly distinct from the remaining Australopithecus. Its characters were clearly hominid. It could, however, not be regarded as a median type, but also manifested a development beyond the human (Knussmann). The drawing gives a reconstruction of one side of a representative of an Australopithecus group (left) and of the Paranthropus group (right). On the right half skull can be seen the cranial crista such as the most powerful individuals of Paranthropus showed. This cranial crista is not however of a pongid shape.

groups and races. Especially well represented was the subfamily of the dryopithecines which unfortunately is documented by only the incomplete remains of bones, fragments of teeth and jaws. It must be assumed that from them are derived the present man-apes, the orang utan from an Indian and gorilla and chimpanzee from African dryopithecines. In view of the astonishing state of development, in the early days, of the man-ape distribution it becomes imperative to ask where and in what manner these hominid-like creatures made their appearance. On this pro-blem of the determination of the time even the dead disagree. The human dentition, according to progressive experts, cannot be derived from the dental structure of the original man-apes, neither could it be derived from that of the dryopithecines. The split among the manlike great apes in the widest sense (Hominoidea) into pongids and hominids may have taken place in the middle Tertiary period 25 million years ago; this means the separation of the anthropoid apes in the more restricted sense (without the gibbon) and the man-like apes. From

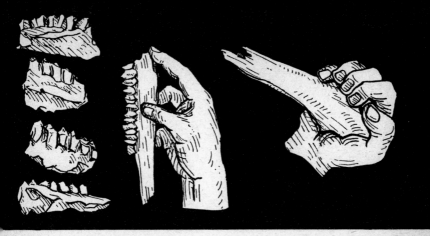

Fig. 36. During the last years before 1959 it had not yet been decided whether Australopithecus was still subhuman or had become a hominid. The opinion was that he used animal bones picked up by chance to kill his prey, to skin it and cut it up and he was not thought capable of intentionally making tools. The illustration shows left: bone fragments, found with Australopithecus in Makapansgat, Central Transvaal. Right: reconstruction of the possible use of the bones as tools (Drawing after photographs by Dart).

there an easy pedigree cannot be traced which runs in a direct sequence to the recent Homo sapiens and the recent great apes. The anthropoid ape-human field of transition must be thought of as an origin for a radiant point whence a wheft or a network of numerous genera, species and sub-species grows in every direction, producing anthropoid apes with human characteristics and man-like creatures with apelike structures. Finally, we see only the sites of accidental finds bound together in a spatial and temporal field of development. The record is full of gaps since the greater part of past living beings remain hidden from us. To trace certain lines of development from these accidental discoveries is a questionable enterprise — and all which has been produced in bygone days is uncertain and easily upset by new discoveries. Yet to be able to proceed with research at all, hypotheses and working theories must be formed, however groundless. From them one must presume that the hominids must have been isolated as an independent branch within the Hominidae. It was the "subhuman phase" of human stock during which in their spiritual development they still remained completely animals. Their scope still lay very near to that of the higher apes. They were still guided by pictorial representations only, combined with an intensive inner awareness of pictures which could be increased to the stage when they could imagine things plastically and also really "saw" objects in imagination. Yet before crossing the spiritual Rubicon, before plucking the fruit of the tree of knowledge, there remained as a fundamental

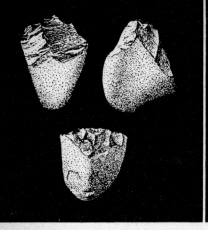

Fig. 37. L. S. B. Leakey, the archaeologist, and his wife together discovered in 1959 in the Olduvai Gorge the nearly complete skull of a special form of the Australopithecines (see p. 10). With the skull of Zinjanthropus boisei Leakey found shaped stone tools. From that moment it became clear that these early men had been not only users but makers of tools. This required a power of abstraction peculiar to man. The Australopithecines had as makers of tools crossed the threshold to humanity. The drawings reproduce the sharp stones which Zinjanthropus fashioned by hitting the jagged sharp edges (after Oakley, Neuville and Ruhlmann).

prerequisite for a future mankind, the erect carriage. Only this would make possible that, by freeing the hands, for grasping and doing away the need for a snout, the skull could itself be re-shaped and the brain case could be enlarged. At this point of time when these tetrapods (quadrupeds) arose and were capable of sustained walking upright as bipeds, is the root of the beginning of mankind to be found. At this time we can perhaps work out for what reasons the quadruped or tetrapod became a biped.

The archeologist and palaeontologist, Louis Seymour Bazelt Leakey, who in 1959 found the Zinjanthropus in the 25 mile long Olduvai Gorge at the edge of the Serengeti Plain, was born at Kabete in Kenya,

as the son of a Missionary, in 1903 and spent much of his childhood in the woven huts of the Kikuyu. At sixteen he went to England and at Cambridge he wrote a work on the Stone Age of Kenya. Now he has the honour of being one of the Elders of the Kikuyu tribe and still thinks, as he says, in the Kikuyu language. As early as his twentieth year he took part in an East African Expedition which was seeking human fossils. In 1931 and 1932 he excavated in this "Dream world for fossil-hunters", in Olduvai Gorge or "the cradle of humanity" as he called it. He found primitive "pebble tools" the makers of which were unknown. With the discovery of this "Oldowan-culture" he made practical attempts to see how a primeval man could

Fig. 38. On this map are marked, according to present knowledge, the world-wide distribution of Australopithecus: from the Transvaal and the Serengeti Plain in East Africa (Olduvai Gorge) through Java to China.

hunt and slay his prey. He crept up to a gazelle and killed it with his bare hands. But he could not succeed in skinning an animal with only his fingers and teeth to help. Only after he had learnt to make a stone chopper in less than four minutes was it possible for him to skin and quarter his prey. Since it was easier to make a new axe than to sharpen a blunt edge Leakey could now explain the abundance of implements in Olduvai Gorge. Even if prehistoric man did outwardly so much resemble an ape he was yet capable of fashioning implements with creative imagination and an intelligence which could only be human. He also became a tool-maker for he had gone over from an exclusively herbivorous regime to a carnivorous diet. Before Leakey had yet made his splendid find of the tool-maker, Zinjanthropus, he had succeeded in 1948, ten years

earlier, in making another discovery. At the Island of Rusinga in the Gulf of Kavirondo, Lake Victoria his wife dug up the skull of a primordial ape which might have existed about 25 or 30 million years ago and which was older than the dryopithicines. Leakey called it „Proconsul africanus" (Hopwood called his first discovery after the chimpanzee named "Consul" in the London Zoo.) Thereupon numerous finds were made in the basin of Lake Victoria Nyanza of these anthropoid ape forms which may well be the most ancient. Of the Proconsulines we now already know three species which range in size from dwarf chimpanzees to gorillas. The Proconsul lacked the supra orbital torus and a simian shelf. With a trace of a chin, small canine teeth and a bodily form which is more slender and graceful than that of modern great apes, Proconsul represented the model of a type whence the Pongids and the hominids, man-apes and man-like beings, could have developed. It was possible that a specifically human line had branched out from this type for Proconsul was not a pronouncedly long-armed brachiator although he was capable of it, he did not posses the limb proportions suitable for that particular adaptation. As tree dwellers by nature they could still leave the thinly wooded forests or groups of trees, their original habitat, to move across the steppes, running upright, and so reach other woods.

From Proconsul until the last part of the Tertiary, the Pliocene, lay a path of development of at least 15 million years which perhaps included a succession of 400,000 generations. It was during this period that those who were making their way towards humanity must have accomplished the upright carriage. And during this time also some ten or eleven million years ago there lived the presumed collateral branch of man, the Oreopithecus, in the peat bogs of the present Tuscan plain of which we wrote on page 7 of this book.

Some ten million years later the Australopithecines were distributed in South Africa, East Africa and in Java. This sub-family of Anthropoids was preserved through several hundreds of thousands of years until at least beyond the beginning of the Günz Ice Age, 600.000 years ago, which corresponds to the Kageran-Pluvial period in Africa (Pluvial periods = periods of heavy precipitation in the tropics and sustropics during the Ice Age). Two genera of the Australopithecines are recognised, the Australopithecus and the Paranthropus. From the Australopithecus genus descends the subspecies Australopithecus africanus africanus, from the place of discovery, Taung in Bechuanaland; and the other species, Australopithecus africanus transvaalensis from Sterkfontein near Johannesburg, Makapansgat in Central Transvaal and from East Africa (probably Zinjanthropus). Of the genus Paranthropus, were found the subspecies robustus robustus from Kromdraai near Johannesburg, Paranthropus robustus crassidens in Swartkranz and Paranthropus palaeojavanicus at Sangiran in Java. The volume of the brain of the Australopithecines was hardly larger than that of modern anthropoid apes — fluctuating between 500 cc and 700 cc whilst the skull capacity of recent great apes does not exceed 685 cc. The form of their cranium deviated from that of the apish, the supra orbital arches were less pronounced than in the great apes, the contraction in the temporal region was less than in the anthropoid apes, the brow was lightly vaulted and the occiput somewhat rounded. Paranthropus, with his greater supra orbital ridges and more pronounced snout formation represented a remarkable type. He was a being which developed past the hominines but yet, as a tool-maker must be classed as a human hominid. The name 'Paranthropus' also means 'near man'. He was neither an ape nor a pronounced anthropoid. By his characteristics he should be placed between the Anthropoid apes and the Australopithicines. Whilst Paranthropus was a pure vegetarian, the members of the Austrapolithecus genus lived as carnivorous hunters and cannibals. Their habitat was the open veldt or a light beech forest northeast of the present Kalahari desert. They practised a big game hunt by the whole tribe on baboons, antelopes and hares, they caught tortoises, lizards, river freshwatercrabs and they killed and devoured their own species. Traces of blackening at some sites seemed to indicate the use of fire but later they were shown to be caused by the action of manganese dioxide. Not only the use of fire separates man from beast. Besides erect carriage the imaginative planning and making of implements is decisive. From the end of the Lower Pleistocene until the Kamasian Pluvial of the Second Glacial period 400,000 years ago implements of pebbles ("pebble tools") were found in Portugal, Morocco, Algeria, Uganda and in North Tanganyika. In the same strata in which the stone artefacts lay were also found skeletal remains of Australopithecus. It could not, however, be proved that, for instance, Australopithecus africanus from Makapansgat was the manufacturer of these stone implements. It was only when the Leakeys in 1959 in the Olduvai Gorge, unearthed a camp site of Zinjanthropus and then found with his skull his stone artefacts as well as the remains of meals—consisting of rodents, reptiles, birds and the young of large mammals—that the true human hominid nature of the Australopithecus species Zinjanthropus was proved.

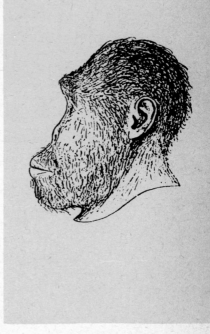

Fig. 39. Reconstructed picture of Paranthropus crassidens, the large-toothed being. He was a human hominid. Even if the volume of his brain hardly exceeded that of a present anthropoid ape, one must still not compare him with the present large apes. His teeth were very human, he probably walked upright and was a tool maker (after Heberer).

Fig. 40. During the Ice Age when cold periods were, in Africa, rainy periods, there existed in South Africa and East Africa savannahs and dry steppes which were the probable habitat of the Australopithecines. The baboons illustrated here were the animals hunted by the African prehominines.

Regarding the true culture of pre-hominines one must resign oneself to the fact that most of it remains closed to us. Besides the remains of meals and the implements everything has gone which could give us some clue to their creative activities; wood, bark, flower decorations, wind screens, mats from vegetable fibres, fish skins and animal pelts have been as little preserved as their prayers, dances, games, feasts, drinks, banquets or their possible manhood rites.

The anthropologist, Egon Freiherr von Eickstedt wrote a "Genealogical History of the Spiritual" an excellent "Palaeopsychology" which deals with the origin and development of the psychical in the manner of and supplied by fundamental works and findings in animal and juvenile psychology. On the attitude to the soul of the Australopithecines he believes himself able to say: "In the way of experience there is dominant throughout a kaleidoscopic inter-related world. Feeling and perception hardly are separated in the world of visions, space and time are just floating environmental qualities from which only the material value, but not its quality or even hours, days or where possible years, have radiated.

Thus the border between I and not-I is only at the border of one's own and actually experienced, perceptible world. As a perception it is a possessive world, beyond lurk the powers of 'I' opponents, the enemy world. Hence cannibalism. But this by no means denotes merely bestial brutality and coarseness which is so erroneously and often ascribed to the beginnings of humanity. Quite the reverse. The thymality within his own circle means just the opposite, tenderness, goodness and cheerfulness, and allows with complete justification the presumption of a picture of intimate family life and the specific teaching of the children, also need of ornament, dance and much happiness. Thus the extremes of feeling swing with the mood between fear and love, and the dread of the unknowable may also have cropped up during lightning, death and dreams perhaps in individuals, yet the sense of being moved by the aesthetic was probably confined to very rare starry nights ... And thus is indicated by supposition in outline, but at least within reasonable limits, the psychogenetic position of the Australopithecines. They are still wading through the hundred million year wide Rubicon, they are in a ford leading nowhere and are stuck at a sandbank of their own from which not even their true hominid urge to murder can help them."

II

THE WAY TO HUMANITY.

A world wide event of cataclysmic dimensions is somehow connected with the appearance of Original Man (Archanthropus) and Ancient Man (Palaeoanthropus) in some unknown manner: a "Klimasturz" (sudden plunge in temperature) or glaciation of world wide dimensions. For three hundred million years, a prodigious time, ice and cold had had in this world a rarity value. In this immense span of time there were no polar ice-caps, the Arctic and the Antarctic were sub-tropicial regions, mountain heights were not snow-covered; no snow, indeed, fell and over the whole circumference of the earth a more or less warm climate prevailed. Geologists asked when this climatic catastrophe could have had its beginning and where its cause could

be sought. To determine the time various methods were employed. But only by nuclear-physical means was a more precise determination of the age of world historical events made possible — it was a technique of absolute time measurement. The geologists had solved one of their problems. The last Ice Age had commenced about one million years ago.

The anthropologists also had a pressing question on their minds, it

Fig. 41. World map of the Glacial Period (Ice Age) after the Tertiary. The greatest advance of the glaciation is light green; the least extension of glaciation in the last glaciation is white. The land spaces which became covered by wind-driven fine sand (loess) are shown by white stippling.

was altogether too remarkable that precisely at the beginning of the Ice Age man should appear, even if he did not quite correspond to modern Homo sapiens. It was but a step to suggest that the apparently sudden

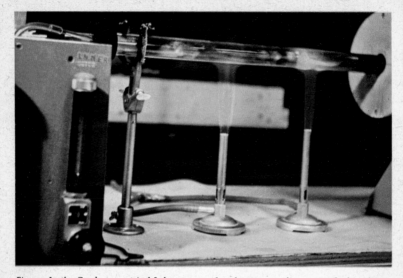

Fig. 42. In the Geochronometrical Laboratory at Yale University of Newhaven U.S.A. the absolute age of fossil remains is determined with the "Gas counter tube". The new procedure developed by Professor H. de Vries of Gröningen in 1958, has a range of some 70,000 years. The father of the radiocarbon method was Professor W. F. Libby who in 1960 deservedly received the Nobel prize for Chemistry for the development of his "C14-method". He still worked with solid carbon and his age determinations did not go beyond 53,000 years. In dead plants and dead animals he could decide by the carbon14 content at what time the remains had been alive. For example, the age of the Florisbad skull from South Africa was measured by the old method; it was more than 41,000 years old. Beyond that the carbon clock was unable to go at that time, so that this skull may be much older. The difficulties of the radio carbon determination are so great because a kilogramme of organic carbon contains only a millionth part of a milli-gramme of C14.

Here a sample is being burnt with oxygen. The air inlets, left, control the oxygen flow. The clear flame in the tube is caused by inflammable gas which emerges from a very small hole in the tip of the test tube. The tube containing the object to be examined lies in the combustion tube. This kind of counter is used at Gröningen and at Yale.

development of man and the climatic change were connected. The German anthropologist, Hans Weinert, expressed this obvious conception concisely with the words: "Without Ice Age no man" — "through the Ice Age comes man". He founded a theory, according to which man developed from chimpanzee-like anthropoid apes: "Under the action of the approaching Ice Age the tropical forest of Europe had to disappear. For anthropoid apes this implies an extraordinary encroachment on their previous condition of life. They had the choice of emigrating or dying out if flight to a better climatic habitat was impossible. As a third resort they could develop from man-apes into the first forms of humanity".

Fig. 43. The open "Bänderton Profile". Such "varves" are an absolute yearly time scale which the earth itself marked with a varying sedimentation at the close of an Ice Age.

This extract repeats a universally held view which even now is repeated in numerous popular presentations, in reconstructed "tableaux vivants" of Ice Age man. The generalized conception of "Man of the Ice Age" necessarily connects the original man and ancient man together with the misfortune of a climate in which, in parts of the world, the mean yearly temperature was reduced, vast masses of water turned to ice and snow, the climatic zones shifted markedly and organic life was either destroyed by cold and ice or was driven back. The man of this extreme time, so one believed, was deeply influenced by the polar cold of ice and snow. Accordingly he was more like an animal than a modern man. At one time man lived not only in the European regions, but in others and to those which he fell back on, he also did not "flee" for a slow retreat which could not come to the knowledge of the respective individual descendants was no flight. In addition, during these tens of hundreds of thousands of years there was no well defined and extreme Ice Age. The generalized concept distorts the true picture. There were many epochs with advancing inland ice and mountain glaciation, which were interrupted by an equal number of warm or Interglacial periods. These lasted a long time and were often warmer than the present post-glacial period. The transitions from cold and warm were spread over such enormous lengths of time and were so gradual that man did not immediately feel them. Through many

generations he adapted himself slowly to his dwindling hunting grounds and just as slowly followed tundras which had again become free of glaciation, voluntarily, for the arctic bogs and moors in front of the ice cap were blessed with easily hunted game and had a great attraction for the people of Europe, Northern Asia and Siberia. This was valid only, however, for those people who lived in front of the glaciated land masses; the greater part of humanity was at that time far distant from the ice and knew nothing at all of ice, snow and severe cold. They lived in fertile, warm or cool and damp, rainy zones. Two thirds of all the land areas of the earth never lay in the extreme climatic zone of the Quaternary Ice Age. The present subtropical desert regions, as, for example, the Sahara, experienced summery Pluvial periods.

But it is precisely in these ice-free areas where man with his cultures has from the beginning of the Ice Age started to develop. The cataclysm of the climate offered to the few million men (or perhaps only the few hundred thousands) on earth far greater land areas with fertile grassy expanses and savannahs than is the case with our present thousands of millions. The game had unlimited grazing lands, the hunter unlimited game. This should be understood and the reason was that the ice froze immence quantities of oceanic water and the level of the oceans sank. At the time of the maximum advance of the ice the level of the sea, according to the latest computations, was

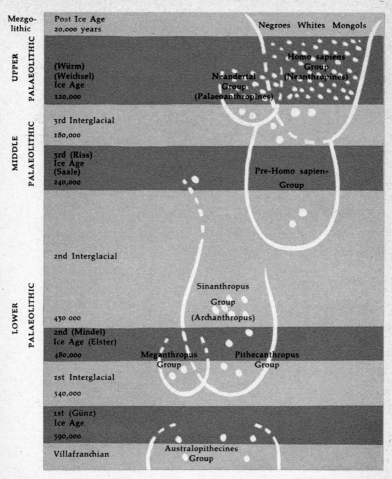

Mezgo-lithic		Post Ice Age 20,000 years	Negroes Whites Mongols

Fig. 44. The drawing represents "steps of human creation during the Ice Age". The Australopithecine group extended from the bottom step (coloured grey) to the 1st warm keriod (I. Interglacial). The age of early man or original man (Archanthropines) followed the Australopithecines, they existed from the 1st Interglacial some 540.000 years ago until almost the end of the long 2nd warm period (II. Interglacial). The Archaic man of the pre-sapiens range followed the early men, still in the 2nd Interglacial. They led, during the 3rd Interglacial in a smooth progress of development, to the immediate predecessors of present day man — upon one side to Neandertal Man and on the other to Homo sapiens (after Asmus).

about 120 m lower than now. Large portions of the Continental shelf, the shelf covered by the sea at present, were uncovered and the islands,

Fig. 45　　HISTORY OF THE DEVELOPMENT OF MAN IN THE QUATERNARY PERIOD I

Table V

	Geological time scale	Years before the present	Archaelogical time table Sequence of cultural groups
	Interglacial-Tegelen (Holland) Pre-Ice Age Danube Ice Age = Villafranchian Several Warm and Cold periods Butley Glacial (England) Kageran Pluvial (East Africa) Nebraskan (U.S.A.)	1–2 m.y. 1 m. years	Oldest cultures: simple hand axes tool maker flaked pebble tools chopping tools
Paleopleistocene	Günz glaciation (Alps) Waybourne = Ice Age (England) Kageran Pluvial (East Africa) Nebraskan (U.S.A.) First Ice Age Retreat of Ocean (North Sea)	600,000	Oldowan culture Hand axe culture Crag industries Late Kafuan
	1. Interglacial Günz Mindel warm period I-Warm period (I = infima = the lowest) Cromer Interglacial (England) Interpluvial (East Africa) Aftonian (East Africa) Advance of Oceans (Mediterranean)	540,000	Cultures with hand axes (bifaced) Abbevillian Early Clacton pre-Chellean
	Mindel glaciation Second Ice Age Elster Ice Age Kamasian Pluvial (East Africa) Kansan (U.S.A.)	480,000	Clactonian Lower Acheulian
Mesopleistocene	Mindel-Riss Interglacial Second warm period O-Warm period (O = optima = the best) Hollstein Interglacial (Northern Germany) Interpluvial (East Africa) Yarmouth (U.S.A.) Middle Interglacial Advance of the oceans (North Sea and Mediterranean)	430,000	Lower Acheulian (Chellean) to Middle Acheulian Middle Clactonian Early Levalloisian Use of fire

The most important fossil human finds	Biological time scale Characteristic mammals	
Australopithecines: Australopithecus Paranthropus	Giant Mastodon Bison of gigantic size Sabre tooth tiger (Machairodus)	
Meganthropus palaeojavanicus Zinjanthropus bosei		
Pithecanthropus modjokertensis (= robustus) Pithecanthropus dubius Heidelberg Man	Southern elephant (Elephas meridionalis) Etruscan rhinoceros (Rhinoceros etruscus) Sabre tooth tiger (Machairodus)	
Gigantopithecus Sinanthropus Pithecanthropus erectus Swanscombe Man Steinheim Man Atlanthropus mauritanicus (Ternifine Man)	Steppe elephant (Elephas trogontherii) Forest elephant (Elephas antiquus) Merck's rhinoceros (Rhinoceros Merckii) Hippopotamus	Early palaeolithic (Early Old Stone Age)

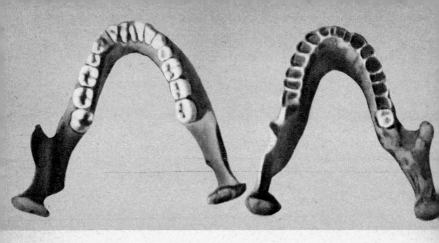

Fig. 46. In these four illustrations are shown left to right: lower jaw of a recent man, Pekin man (Sinanthropus pekinensis), lower jaw of Giganthropus and lower jaw of a present day female gorilla.

reefs, sand banks and coasts dried. England was joined to Europe as Siberia was with Alaska through the Bering land bridge. A large part of Indonesia was mainland and was almost joined to Australia. Malaya and the present Indonesian islands formed a continental bridge which lay in the then still shallow waters separating Australia and New Guinea from Southern Asia. It is a fairy tale occasioned by ignorant views, that the hominids became true humans after a struggle with a ruthless, cruel, implacable glacial environment. Quite to the contrary, they developed in positively paradisiacal surroundings. The climate was favourable to them throughout long periods and their hunting grounds were unrestricted.

With the discovery of Zinjanthropus one can regard the "Southern apes" as pre-human or early men. They introduced the fossil story of the Ice Age. The palaeontologist, Gustav von Koenigswald, bought in 1935, in Chinese chemists' shops a whole series of teeth which were there offered for sale as medicine, to be pulverised and swallowed. In some of these "dragone teeth" he believed he detected the remains of a giant ape. Later similar teeth were dug up in inaccessible mountain caves in South China, together with remains of game killed with weapons. In the Linchang cave in the South China province of Kwangsi two lower jaws were first recovered. Like the

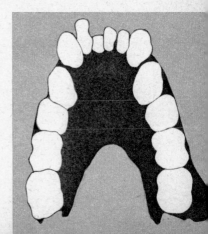

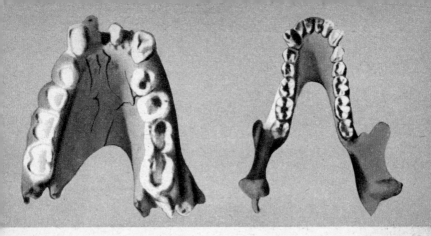

teeth, so the remains of the jaws were also of an unlikely size. Weidenreich, a German anatomist and anthropologist, after the last war, unwittingly provided a world sensation. In 1945 he investigated and described the "dragons" teeth, he thought that they belonged to a man or an anthropoid. On the strength of three teeth he reconstructed a gigantic man. The human giants were said to be twice the size of an average man with a weight of more than three hundredweight. According to von Koenigswald's ideas Gigantopithecus was a Giganthropus and should be regarded as the forefather of all primitive and modern men. "The more primitive the forms", wrote Weidenreich, "the more gigantic are their dimensions".With that he contradicted the conception of his colleague of fifty years earlier: The Basle anatomist, Kollmann, believed then that only dwarfs or pygmies could have been the oldest men. Now, however, Adam had become a giant, although such a giant could by no means have walked erect.

Afterwards, in 1957/58, a third lower jaw bone was found in a side passage at Linchang. Now there were three lower jaws and numerous teeth as evidence for the existence of a creature which had been either a gigantic ape or a gigantic man. But neither a Giganthropus nor a Gigan-

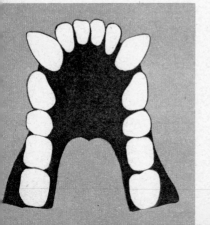

Fig. 47 and 48. In these two drawings Prof. G. Heberer has compared the lower jaw of a Giganthropus (on left) to that of a gorilla. Both are only drawn as far as the 2nd molar since the lower jaw of Giganthropus is broken off at that point. After the first dig in South China in which two lower jaws were found yet a third was recovered in 1957/8.

topithecus can be deduced from the dentition only. There is no fundamental, constant proportion between the size of teeth and bodily size. Also, evolution does not begin with giant forms but may end with them. From normal sized reptiles came the monster dinosaurs, from small mammals grew mammoths or giant deer, from small dog-sized horses came the horse of today. The most telling objection to Weidenreich's hypothesis was, however, this: the dating and determination of the age of the stratum in which the bony remains of Gigantopithecus were found destroyed the genealogical tree which he compiled. According to this, the ape-men (Pithecanthropus) emerged from the giant men of South China and finally evolved into Australian aborigines. Simultaneously the giant men had sent out another branch of development; it was supposed to lead through Pekin Man (Sinanthropus) to "certain Mongoloid groups". These two series of development were too simple an answer. Gigantopithecus lived during the Middle Pleistocene in the second warm epoch *after* Pithecanthropus and long after the very human Australopithecenes.

The pressing question whether in the matter of Gigantopithecus we are dealing with an ape or a man-like creature was answered by G. Heberer. "The vacillating verdict of the experts as to whether Gigantopithecus represents a hominid or a pongid again underlines the fact that 'Darwin was right'. Pongids and hominids form one common historical entity,

and the hominids have as their ancestors an 'ancient member' of the pongids. A decision can only be arrived at by means of new discoveries but also, perhaps, through exact investigation of the fragments available. However this may turn out in any event there never have been in the genealogical history of man giants with an erect carriage." Twelve kilometres northward from Surakarta in

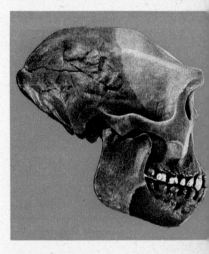

Fig. 49. Pithecanthropus modjokertensis (robustus) reconstruction (after Weidenreich) and drawing (after Grahmann). The German anthropologist F. Weidenreich added to the

Java near the village of Sangiran, fossil bones were dug up by Gustav von Koenigswald and his authorized collectors in the years 1936 to 1939, which undoubtedly had human features. At the end of 1939 they found, in addition, yet another upper jaw and the posterior portion of the skull of a very coarse and stocky individual. Koenigswald called this upright being with retreating forehead and mighty brow-ridges, Pithecanthropus modjokertensis. Weidenreich, who, at the outbreak of the second war was working with von Koenigswald in Peking, gave it the name of Pithecanthropus robustus on account of its size and massiveness. Java man lived during the Lower Pleistocene, perhaps already during the first Ice Age, but

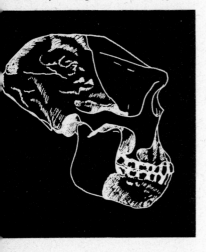

parts of an adult skull a lower jaw which had been discovered in the same stratum in 1956. In the illustration the preserved bones are dark.

certainly by the time of the first Interglacial. So it may be possible that he was a contemporary of the last Australopithecines. Without the least doubt he was a man, a primeval man, an Archanthropus.

Haeckel had in the last century the erroneous idea that man is immediately descended from the gibbons.

In the habitat of the present gibbon in the South Eastern part of tropical Asia he believed that there must be a "missing link", a link between ape and man, a being who walks erect, an "ape-man". The Dutch army doctor, Eugen Dubois, believed in this false hypothesis. Entirely for that reason he had himself transferred to Java in order to find Haeckel's fantastic missing link — and he really dug it out! This is one of the most romantic events in the history of palaeontology, which is already full of incredible accidental finds.

When Dubois made his discoveries in 1891/92, near the village of Trinil in central Java, in the bed of the River Solo, he immediately gave it the name of Pithecanthropus. He had found a very much younger "ape-man" than Koenigswald did in the years 1936 to 1939 with his Pithecanthropus modjokertensis. — 100,000 years divide the "robust ape-man" from the "erect walker" of the Dutch doctor. But the older ape-man, with his sloping brow, his mighty browridges was also, in spite of his massiveness, very likely an erect walker and a Homo of a very primitive kind.

If Koenigswald's finds — a child's skull from Modjokerto and several lower jaws from Sangiran — were the oldest fossil human remains which have been found hitherto in Asia, so, too, had Europe, since October 1907, its primitive man, Homo heidelbergensis. He lived about 500,000 years ago in a warm climate. Ten kilometres southeastward from

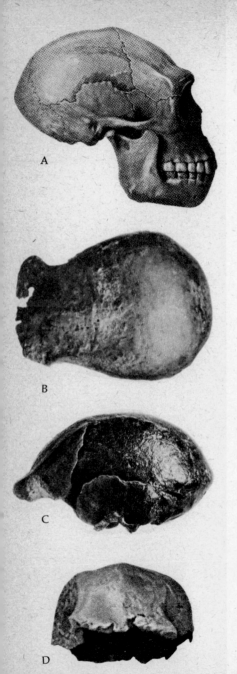

A

B

C

D

Heidelberg in the Elsenztal near the district of Mauer, the wonderfully preserved "Heidelberg lower jaw", in which all the sixteen teeth were still present, was recovered — and these teeth belonged to a dentition which was thoroughly human. Even if they are very big, far and away larger than man's today, and if all indication of a chin is absent, even so Heidelberg man was a true man. This oldest fossil remains of a European is that of a primitive and heavily built being. He seems to have had some similarity to Pithecanthropus of Java — but he resembles also another primitive man, Sinanthropus, the Man of China or Pekin Man.

The story of the discovery of Sinanthropus might well have been due to the imagination of a romantic novelist. The physician K. A. Haberer early in this century like von Koenigswald after him, bought in Chinese chemists' shops numerous fossil bones and teeth which he sent to the palaeontologist, Max Schlosser at Munich. After a meticulous examination of the bone remains he prophecied the discovery of early Pleistocene man or hominid of the first Ice Age. He formulated the — for that time — monstrous assertion in the following words: "Even if the bad state of preservation of this tooth does not enable us to give any clear decision on its systematic position, yet I feel it my duty never-

Fig. 50. Pithecanthropus erectus the "erect-walking ape-man" from Java, A) skull reconstruction (after Weinert), B, C, D) the original vault of the cranium from three sides (after Dubois).

theless to discuss this object instead of passing it over in silence. The object of this communication is to direct the attention of later investigators, who may be unable to excavate in China, to the fact that either a new fossil anthropoid or a Tertiary man, or even a Palaeopleistocene man may be found."

Such an idea, founded on a tooth bought in a Chinese chemist's shop, seemed so absurd that Schlosser's report was not discussed at all. The tooth was then lost. Twenty-five years later, in 1921, the Swedish geologist, Andersson, was prospecting in China for useful minerals. In a cave near the village of Choukoutien, 40 km south of Pekin, he found pieces of quartz which did not belong to the geological stratum in which they lay. He therefore postulated

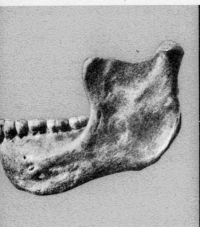 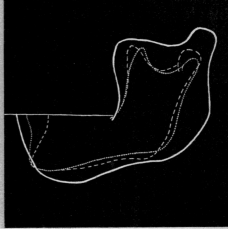

Fig. 51. This "Heidelberg lower jaw" (after Mollison) is up to now the oldest human fossil found in Europe. Homo heidelbergensis lived more than half a million years ago in an Interglacial age.

Fig. 52. For comparison, three profile drawings of different lower jaws are superimposed: the firm outline belongs to the Heidelberg lower jaw; the interrupted line is that of a recent European and the dotted line is that of a negro (after Gieseler). The Heidelberg lower jaw was at its recovery in an astonishingly good state of preservation; all 16 teeth were present — and they were unequivocally those of a human being.

the presence of early human beings who must have brought the quartz to make tools or weapons. After further wearisome digging he actually discovered two human teeth. In 1927 the Canadian anatomist, Davidson Black, received from the Rockefeller Foundation a grant to enable him to dig there intensively for two years. From April until October 1927 quantities of animal fossils were recovered, but no human remains. At last, a colleague

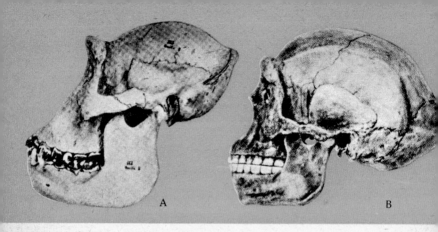

A   B

Fig. 53. In this illustration is the reconstructed skull B) of Sinanthropus pekinensis the China Man from Pekin with the skull A) of a gorilla (both of them after Weidenreich), C) of a Neandertal Man (after Weinert) and D) a modern man (after Weidenreich) compared.

of Black's, the Swedish geologist Bohlin, found one single human molar. Quite in Schlosser's style he named it "the most important tooth in the world" and on this discovery alone founded a primitive human

Fig. 54. Recovered skull portions of Sinanthropus pekinensis A) skull from above, B) skull still in the rock, C) skull front view, D) parietal bone (after Black).

group which he called Sinanthropus, although the remains of not a single individual other than the tooth had as yet been found. A year later, Bohlin succeeded, in collaboration with the Chinese Professor W. C. Pei, in recovering skull fragments, more teeth and two lower jaws of the Man of China or Pekin Man. In 1929, Professor Pei found, indeed, a cranium of the most ancient "Chinese" who flourished 400,000 years ago.

In the course of ten years from 1927 until 1937 they recovered the skeletal remains of 40 individuals of both sexes and amongst them the

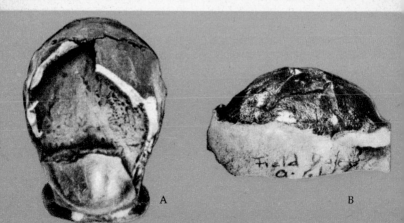

A   B

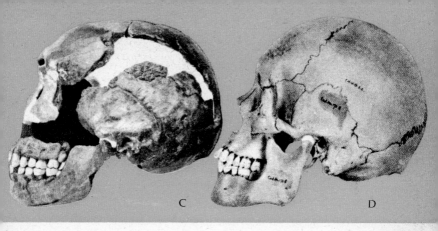

C

D

skeletons of 15 children. The skulls throughout showed heavy damage bones were split open to get at the marrow. The traces of blows on the skulls, the broken arm and leg bones, the careless disposal of the killed (mixed together with remains of animals), left only one meaning to the cave: it had been the meeting place of head-hunters and cannibals.

After the last war the Chinese resumed the digs with profit. In the cave during 1949 and 1951 further Sinanthropus remains were recovered (5 teeth and limb fragments). Artefacts of Pekin Man were found made of quartz and erratic rocks. Compared to implements of later men, of the Stone Age (for instance with those of Neandertaloid Crimean men from the Kiik cavern near Simferopol who lived 200,000 years later than Pekin Man) one has to admit that the implements from the Crimea are finer, more elegant. Nevertheless, the tool culture of the primitive men from China were worthy of wonder. The chopping tool industries near Peking are, incidentally, related to quite similar tool cultures, which were dug up in Java, Siam, Burma, Malaya, South Africa and East Africa.

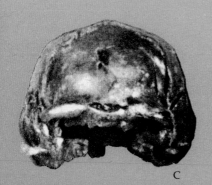

C

D

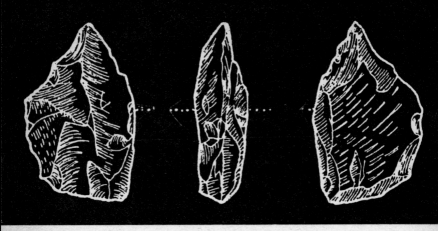

Fig. 55. A comparison of stone inplements of Sinanthropus — this page — with those of a much more recent Stone age Man from the Crimea (p. 75) (after Grahmann).

So Sinanthropus pekinensis was a tool-maker, killed and devoured his fellow beings and even knew the use of fire — these were all typical human peculiarities; no animal is capable of making implements by design or, like Cain, of slaying his blood brother.

Australopithecus from Makapansgat had been lent the specific name of Prometheus, for it was believed that he had perhaps made fires — among the first to do so. But it was Sinanthropus of Choukoutien who had really used fire for the first time. One must take care, however, in assuming that only the use of fire is a sign of truly becoming human. The making of artefacts already heralds the human phase and before the use

Fig. 56. Plan of the site of Sinanthropus pekinensis. The Choukoutien cave lies near the village of Choukoutien 40 km southwestward of Pekin (Peiping). It is the terminus of a branch railway which connects the surrounding coal mines and sandstone quarries with Pekin (after Teilhard de Chardin and Young).

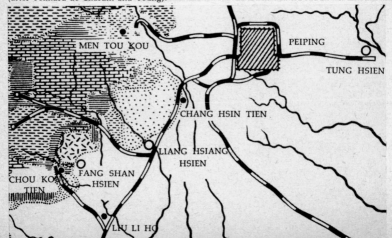

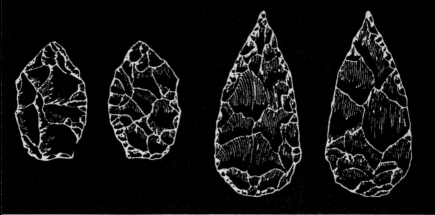

of fire, even up to half a million years before the promethean died, a human being made useful implements.

Yet artefact *and* fire, as well as cannibalism as a customary dish or customary ritual, place a man in advance, who knows precisely that the tool's edge used once will be useful again tomorrow, that the burning, warming fire can be fanned into a blaze again. This thinking foresight, coupled with a lack of inhibition in killing off a fellow being — the natural bent to overcome whoever tries to thwart it — this bears witness to an almost civilized domesticated man who even transferred himself to a "household state".

The primitive Men of China, the Pithecanthropus-Sinanthropus group, also had an uncle in North Africa. Whilst Professor Pei still dug in the Choukoutien cave, the French palaeontologist, C. Arambourg, discovered the "Palikao Man of Ternifine". He bears the scientific name of Atlanthropus mauritanicus, the Atlas man

of Mauritania. Before his discovery in 1954 there had been found in Algeria, in Morocco and at the edge of the desert, traces of a still older primitive man from the beginning of the Ice Age, in the shape of roughly hewn stone artefacts. Since they had been fashioned from river pebbles they belonged to a "pebble culture" — but no bone remains of the men who had once upon a time used them were found. Only when Arambourg began his search by pumping out a sandpit near Ternifine, 17 km from Mascara in Algeria (near Oran), did he discover, up to 1955, three lower jaws and a part of a cranium with numerous animal remains and more than one hundred implements of quartzite, limestone and flint. By means of the rich collection of fauna which was found at the site, hippopotamus, giraffe, rhinoceros, wild horse and sabre toothed tiger, the age of the Palikao Man could be determined pretty accurately: he lived at least 400,000 years ago at the beginning of the mid-Pleistocene. If he did not

Table VI

	Geological time scale	Years before the present	Archaegological time scale Sequence of cultural groups
Middle Pleistocene	Riss Ice Age, Glacial Saale Ice Age (North Germany) Kanjeran, Pluvial (East Africa) Illinoian (U.S.A.) Retreat of oceans (North Sea, Mediterranean)	240,000	Late Clactonian Acheulean Levalloisian
	Riss-Würm Interglacial Third and last warm period U — Warm period (ultima = last) Eemian. Interglacial North Germany) Interpluvial (East Africa) Sangamon (U.S.A.) Advance of oceans	180,000 According to latest determin- ations of age 80,000 to 70,000	Late Acheulian Middle Levalloisian Leaf point culture Older blade cultures Cultures with bifaces Micoquian, Late Acheulian Early Mousterian
Upper Pleistocene	Würm Ice Age — Glacial Weichsel Ice Age = (North Germany) Gamblian Pluvial (East Africa) Wisconsin (U.S.A.) Würm I—stage (Early Würm)	70,000	Late Levalloisian Late Mousterian
	Warm swing (Interstadial or Göttweiger Interstadial Würm II stage (Main Würm) Würm III stage (Late Glacial) Alleröd Interstadial End of last glaciation Retreat of oceans	44,000 20,000 15,000 11,000 10,300	Aurignacian Solutrean Magdalenian
Holocene	Postglacial After the Ice Age	10,000 5,000 4,000	Middle Stone Age (Mesolithic) Late Stone Age (Neolithic) Metal ages Bronze Age and Iron Age

The most important human fossil finds	Biological scale Characteristic mammals	
Casablanca Man Africanthropus (?)	Mammoth (Elephas Primigenius) Woolly rhinoceros (Rhinoceros tichorhinus) Reindeer (Rangifer tarandus)	Early Palaeolithic
Rhodesian Man (Broken Hill, Saldanha) Fontéchevade Pre Neandertal Man Weimar-Ehringsdorf Krapina Ganovce Saccopastore Ngangdong Man Palestine Neandertal Man (?)	Bush elephant Mercks rhinoceros Cave bear (Ursus spelaeus)	Meso Palaeolithic
Palestine Man Neandertal Man	Mammoth Woolly rhinoceros Reindeer Musk ox (Ovibus moschatus)	
Brünn Cromagnon Grimaldi races Wadjak Upper Cave at Choukoutien Asselar Olduvai		Neopalaeolithic
Recent Man		

correspond quite to the Pithecanthropus from Java or the Sinanthropus of China, he was at least related
to them. The most astonishing part
of it was, however, that his tools,
hand axes, choppers, flakes of quartzite and flint far surpassed the
"chopping tool culture" of the Man
of China. For the first time a Pithecanthropus - Sinanthropus type had
reached the first greater and higher
step in culture of the palaeolithic
age — the Acheulian which is represented by carefully manufactured
hand axes.

However incomplete our discoveries
of human fossils may be they yet
provide the possibility for a formula
embracing a wide field on the genealogical connection between lemurs,
anthropoid apes and hominids. A
relative scheme such as Professor
Heberer suggested and extended by
means of another diagram on the
unfolding of the true men, can only
be valid as a preliminary arrangement: "At this time only specula-
tive solutions are possible. At any
moment we must be prepared to re-
model a picture such as this 'provisional picture', if new material
necessitates it." (G. Heberer). Nevertheless, one can gather from the
picture that three human branches
developed nearly independently: primitive man (from the Pithecanthropus-Sinanthropus type), archaic men
(within the compass of Neandertal
Man) and modern Men (the Sapiens
group). Homo sapiens — and sapiens
means the knowing, intelligent — we
encounter in Steinheim Man a new,

adaptable, world-exploring and direc-
ting type, of wonderful bodily grace.
He was discovered in 1933 in a gravel pit near Steinheim on the Murr
(a tributary of the Neckar) by its
owner, Sigrist. The Steinheim skull
consists of a cranium and facial parts
without the lower jaw. Sigrist left
it untouched in its stratum and in-
formed the palaeontologist, F. Berckhemer, at once; he hardened the fra-
gile and very precariously placed
skull with acetone and shellac during
the course of removal. It was only
by these means that the valuable
skull was removed from the stratum
in which it was found without damage. The importance of the discovery of the Steinheim skull has
not diminished to this day. Steinheim Man lived approximately 300,000
years ago at the end of the second
Interglacial. The cause of the death
of this man could be clearly seen in
the depression on the left temple:
the Homo steinheimensis, probably
a young female, was killed by vio-
lence. Cannibals had enlarged the
foramen magnum and had detached
the head from the trunk, to reach
the brain.

Although the Steinheim skull may
seem primitive — with very pronounced brow-ridges and broad nose—
it still resembles modern man, with
its graceful shape, with the canine
fossa common only in man, with

Fig. 58. The graphic representation composed
by Prof. G. Heberer of Göttingen of the
ontological relations between apes and men,
together with a diagram representing the
unfolding of true men after the overcoming
of the "Beast-Man" field of transition.

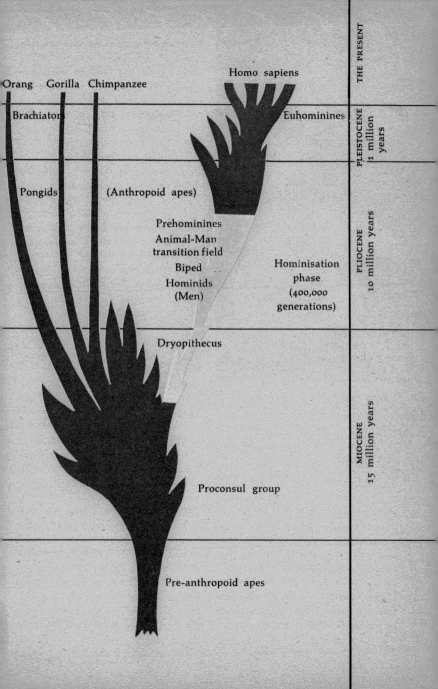

Orang Gorilla Chimpanzee

Homo sapiens

Brachiators

Euhominines

Pongids

(Anthropoid apes)

Prehominines
Animal-Man
transition field
Biped
Hominids
(Men)

Hominisation
phase
(400,000
generations)

Dryopithecus

Proconsul group

Pre-anthropoid apes

THE PRESENT

PLEISTOCENE
1 million
years

PLIOCENE
10 million years

MIOCENE
15 million years

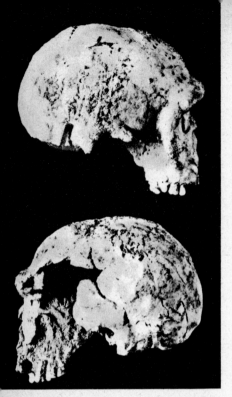

Fig. 59. The skull of Steinheim Man (after Berckhemer) who is about 200,000 years older than Neandertal Man, shows, besides primitive characteristics, astonishing similarity to Homo sapiens. From such a form one can imagine a divergence into a sapiens and a Neandertal humanity. Equally one can fit the Steinheim Man into the development series of Homo sapiens — if the division had occurred earlier.

its "Europoid facial structure", to an astonishing degree quite the reverse of the Neandertaler who first appeared long after the Steinheimer. Homo neandertalensis could hardly be a forefather of Homo sapiens — much more likely was it the considerably older Homo steinheimensis in the middle Pleistocene.

The primitive men from the Choukoutien cave near Pekin, the mountain caves in South China, from Java and North Africa were not followed by the Steinheimer — although in our chronology he should take up this place. The much later Neandertal Man represented Palaeoanthropines. This delicately boned but inferior type of man with his retreating brow and his mighty brow ridges, first appeared about 200,000 years after Steinheim Man. He died out as a specialized form in a blind alley of development whilst Homo sapiens broke through. He had had, however, like Sapiens, his forebears, the pre-Neandertalers. Fossil information from Thuringia, Croatia and Italy testify to this. The Neandertaler from the last Ice Age had had forerunners from the last Interglacial (warm period) who were more finely and delicately formed.

It would be merely confusing to discuss all discoveries here which support, on the one hand pre-Neandertal and on the other the existence of the pre-Sapiens men. There were the pre-Hominines and the pre-Neandertal men and the pre-modern men who lived before the ancient Homo neandertalensis. During the last warm period both forms even lived side by side, yet modern man never issued from the Neandertal line. He emerged from his own independent primitive pre-Sapiens group.

The Steinheimer and the Heidelberger were not the only pre-Sapiens men to appear so early. In 1935/36 the English dental surgeon, Marston, was able to recover from a gravel pit — the "Barnfield Pit" at Swanscombe near London — the remains of the skull of a man. It was as old as the Steinheim skull. G. M. Morant wrote with authority on the Swanscombe find "So far as can be seen the Swanscombe and the Steinheim skulls are very similar and it is not unlikely that this group belonged to the direct ancestors of Homo sapiens or that at least they stood closer to him than Homo neandertalensis."

Finally, in 1947 the skull fragments of two adults from the last Interglacial were unearthed by G. Henri-Martin in the Grotte de Fontéchevade in the Department of the Charente in France. Dr. G. Kurth assessed them as follows: "In any event after the two excellent monographs on the Fontéchevade finds no valid doubt can be raised thereon that independent development to Homo sapiens may already be very old, but the classical European Neandertaler can on no account be dragged into the direct line of forebears of Homo sapiens."

In the hard limestone of the twenty kilometre long Mount Carmel range in Palestine south of Haifa there are numerous caves, of which two became very famous: Mugharet-es-Skhul (Goats cavern) and Mugharet-et-Tabun (Oven cavern) which are called shortly Skhul and Tabun caves. In 1931/32 very fruitful ex-

Fig. 60. Plan of the site of the Steinheim Man's discovery, Ludwigsburg near Stuttgart. The white spot demotes the flood plain of the river Murr.

Fig. 61. The gravel pit at Steinheim on the Murr, a tributary of the Neckar, in which in 1933 the skull of Steinheim Man, Homo steinheimensis, was found (after Berckhemer).

Fig. 62. Distribution chart of finds of fossil humans (redrawn after Heberer).

● Archanthropine Group:
Pithecanthropus and others

○ Neanthropine Pre-sapiens forms:
Sapiens types with fossil ancestors

■ Neandertal- and Pre-Neandertal-Group

□ Rhodesian-Saldanha-Group

cavations were carried out by British and U. S. researchers. In the Skhul cave the skeletal remains of ten individuals were found, men, women and children, and in the Tabun cave, among others, the skeletal remains of a thirty year-old female. Probably these fossils derive from the last warm period. Their importance rests in that the Palestine men from Mount Carmel are no classic Neandertalers. The men from the Skhul cave come near to the Sapiens type, the Tabun woman resembles the pre-Neandertaler. The German anthropologist, Professor Wilhelm Gieseler, adjudged the Carmel men comprehensively. "They represent no uniform, normally varying, human form. They are either the result of a cross between Neandertaler and sapiens-like men or they must absolutely be completely separated into two groups. One may regard them as a hybrid group, as did Heberer and Snow, if one is convinced that the most important representatives (Skhul and Tabun) were contemporary... It is all the same, however, whether one regards the Carmel men as a cross or as two seprarate groups, one thing will in

83

Fig. 63. A diorama in the Natural History Museum in Chicago, Ill. U.S.A. showing the reconstructed picture of the life of a family group of Neandertal Men. How they may have lived in the last Ice Age. As a model for this reconstruction, finds on the Rock at Gibraltar were used (after Blaschke).

any event be confirmed through them and that is the existence of the pre-Sapiens in the Middle East." That man had lived before the assumed last world catastrophe, the Deluge, was at the begining of last century a bold and revolutionary statement. In 1829/30 Dr. Schmerling had dug up in the cave of Engis the skull of a juvenile Neandertaler. A Frenchman, Tournal, in 1827 laid bare human skeletons, together with the bones of cave bears and reindeer, in caves in Southern France. Boucher de Perthes dug up on the Somme tools of Palaeolithic men which he had found near the skeletal remains

of ancient elephants. Edouard Lartet discovered · in the caves of the des Vézère valley engravings on mammoth ivory. The actual scientific fossil history of man first began, however, with the discovery in August 1856 of human skeletal remains in cave clay from the Neandertal, traversed by the Düssel between Elberfeld and Düsseldorf. In this year a quarry owner bestowed upon a teacher of natural history, Professor Carl Fuhlrott, some fossil human remains (vault of the cranium, two humeri (upper arm bones), parts of lower arms and of the two femurs, and a fragment of a pelvis. They came from one of the caves in the limestone cliffs of the Düssel valley and from the "Feldhofer Kirchen" cave. Fuhlrott recognised them at once as human remains and assumed for them "the probability of ante-deluvian age and at the same time of a primitive typical form of our genus."

As in our history there is no "the human" so also one cannot speak of "the Neandertaler". Under Homo neandertalensis is to be understood a group of humans or a circle of forms which has been reconstructed from the fossil remains of about 130 individuals. They may have lived for 60,000 years in a sequence of some 2,400 generations. In this time their heritage of characteristics can by means of mutations and selection have materially altered and a single fixed type would hardly be able to sustain itself. Their general characteristics are: the forehead only slightly vaulted, the heavy brow ridges, a head which is not quite freely movable, supported by a strong cervical musculature, overhanging between wide shoulders. With the marked brow ridges, the retreating forehead, the face with a canine fossa he was the extreme 'classical' Neandertaler as distinct from the pre-Neandertaler of the last Inter-glacial age who was in some respects less different from modern man. The most important finds of classical Ne-andertalers were made at the follow-ing sites: Gibraltar, Neandertal, Spy in Belgium, La Chapelle aux Saints, Le Moustier, La Quina, La Ferassie

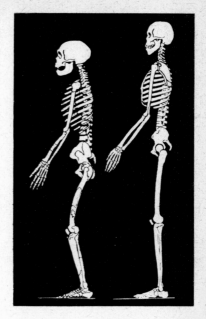

Fig. 64. Here is the reconstructed skeleton of the Neandertal Man from La Chapelle aux Saints (left) to compare with a recent man (after Boule). Massive, coarse with a long broad lower jaw without chin, with short, bent figure and a barrel shaped chest — this is what the, approx. 160 cm. tall, man looked like, muscular but delicate boned, a true Ice Age palaeanthropine who never reached the balance and grace of present man.

in France and Monte Circeo in Italy.

Neandertal Man was not able to attain — as a specialised "end pro-duct" of the branch — to the mobile versatility, the refinement and "mo-dernity" of the present day man or to propagate them himself. "He is not the father of Homo sapiens", so writes Professor Gieseler about him, "but his deceased uncle, in whose demise Sapiens man probably assisted pretty actively by capturing

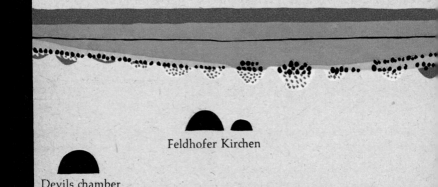

Feldhofer Kirchen

Devils chamber

| More recent loess, clay | More recent loess with "border" | Oligocene displaced | Mass lime | Older loess with coal |

Fig. 65. A sketch of the southern slopes of the Neandertal-Klamm southward of the town of Mettmann between Elberfeld and Düsseldorf. The caves marked in this cross section have now disappeared because of the work of the limestone quarries. In the cave marked "Feldhofer Kirchen" were found in 1856 the skeletal remains of Neandertal Man.

his caves and hunting grounds. Whether Neandertal Man was extirpated without leaving heirs in another question The possibility should not be turned down out of hand that one or another Neandertaler had interbred with the insurgent Sapiens men."

Since, in the last Ice Age, Northern Europe and the North American Continent were glaciated, there prevailed in Iraq, as in all the Middle East, a cold, damp climate — for there the Ice Age was a "Rain Age". From this time and even from the last Interglacial age there originated

men, whose fossil bones the Smithsonian Archeological Expedition of Washington, U.S.A., led by R. S. Solecki, dug up in the Shanidar Cave in Kurdistan, Northern Iraq in 1957. The cave lies 760 m. above sea-level in the Zagros Mountain Range on the slope of a tributary valley of the Great Zab. The pillared hall of a thousand square metre area and 14 m. height is sheltered from the harsh northerly winds and lies near springs of water. For more than 100,000 years (at present by Kurdish goatherds) it has been used as a shelter. In the years 1951 to 1953 the cave floor was dug by archaeologists to 14 m. below the present surface level down to solid rock. This exposed the profile of human culture reaching back to the middle Palaeolithic age. Solecki dug up three

Horses stable

| Oldest cleft filling | Coal and gravel various ages |

skeletons of adult Neandertalers and over each skeleton lay pieces of rock. The excavator presumed that during an earthquake rock fragments from the roof were shaken loose and slew the Neandertalers. It is interesting, incidentally, that in one of the Shanidar skulls healed wounds were found: probably they came from heavy blows on the left side of the eye — signs of survival from a previous fight.

In a stratum at 8.7 m below the surface and nearly 5 m below the three adult skeletons (which in 1955, had not yet been found), lay the greatly disturbed skeleton of a child about eight months old. The characteristics of the child from Shanidar indicated a different Neandertal race, an older "subspecies" — and the stratum in which the child lay was also of an older estimated age than that in which the adults lay. The characters of the child did not yet possess the specialisation of the extreme classical Neandertaler. These older pre-Neandertalers seem to have been closely related to the immediate forebears of present man. The Shanidar child was found in a crouching position and had perhaps been buried in the ordinary way. Since Neandertal children have been frequently found at other places — as on the Rock of Gibraltar — it was considered safe to assume that this ancient human interred his juvenile dead with particular tenderness and care.

Nowadays, and in view of the latest finds, one can speak of a worldwide distribution of Neandertal man who had split up into many branches who had, however, not the slightest thing to do with the present human races. He was at home in North Africa, Palestine, Central Asia and in the Crimea. The "fringe position" of the small West European Neandertal group becomes clear when, according to v. Eicksted, "They wandered up a blind alley, a blind alley geographically and morphologically. When the last icy prominences from the north intruded upon them, this broad nosed southern form was already in grave danger, when in addition Homo sapiens also followed, over the steppes which were extending from the East, he was lost." With the decline of the Neandertalers began the era of modern man. From the path of development

Fig. 66. The Shanidar cave in Iraqi Kurdistan. It was the show place and the site of discoveries of the Smithsonian Institution of Washington U. S. A. Expedition under the leadership of R. S. Solecki which here made the important finds of Neandertal Man.

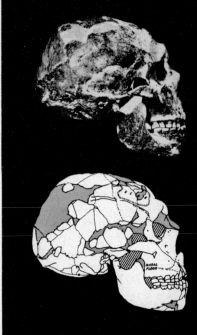

Fig. 67. The skull photographed and described by T. D. Stewart, Curator of Physical Anthropology, Smithsonian Institution, of an adult Neandertal Man "Shanidar I". Right view (photo and drawing). "Full face" wrote Stewart in 1959 "every lineament is as primitive as in the 'classical' Neandertal Man." In this skull healed wounds from heavy blows are the traces of a fight which he survived.   ▷

Fig. 68. Cross section through the strata of the Shanidar cave which contained several human cultures, in the course of a hundred millennia, in the form of artefacts and human remains (redrawn after Solecki).

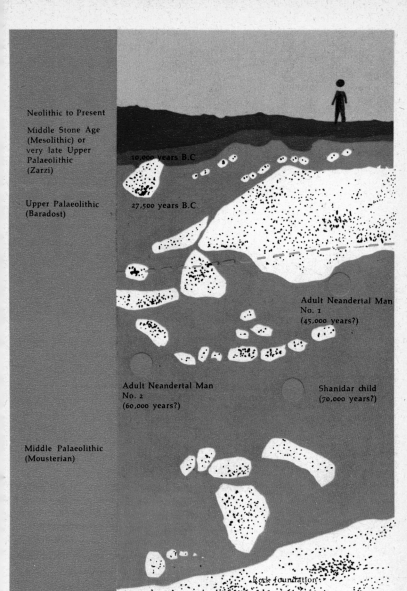

Neolithic to Present

Middle Stone Age
(Mesolithic) or
very late Upper
Palaeolithic
(Zarzi)

10,000 years B.C

Upper Palaeolithic
(Baradost)

27,500 years B.C

Adult Neandertal Man
No. 1
(45,000 years?)

Adult Neandertal Man
No. 2
(60,000 years?)

Shanidar child
(70,000 years?)

Middle Palaeolithic
(Mousterian)

Rock foundation

89

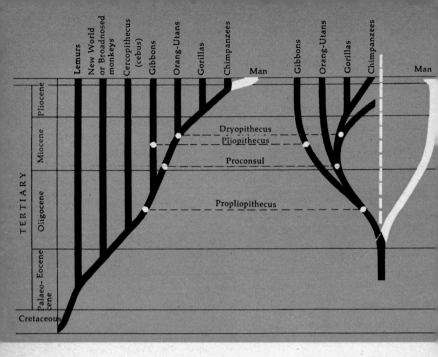

Fig. 69. Two different genealogical trees; the two concepts which show the relationship of the primates: Left by H. Weinert, right H. F. Osborn's. If Oreopithecus bambolii after Hürzeler were added to the same figures in his proper temporal place (turn of the Mio-Pliocene) then Weinert's tree would have to be changed.

which he had to traverse until he became the Homo sapiens recens of modern times we do not really know much. The discoveries are scarce and incomplete and new finds may at any time bring new light into the gloom in which the history of man is plunged.

Amongst the deposits (moraines) from Ice Age glaciers which today still cover wide areas impenetrably, there may rest witnesses of age-old cultures which developed in former steppes, foothills and their valleys, in riverine regions long dried up, in periods of time which would make nonsense of the greater part of our known human history. The continental shelves recaptured by the seas tens of thousands of years ago could be the tombs of former men who, as hunters or fishermen, lived near the coast. In the permafrost of Siberia, under the present peat bogs, in the sandy shoals of the Dogger Bank or in the English Channel and beneath the waters of the Malay Archipelago traces of departed human existence are conceivable which we can no longer reach. Yet no scientist thinks of complaining at the incompleteness of the discoveries, or of folding his arms and awaiting new, more complete fossil prehistoric information. With perspicacity, high deductive power and exact study of the individual documents and their most intimate details the finds may be brought together in a large-scale rearrangement. From such preliminary pedigrees" the researcher obtains the inducement to fruitful theorising. It has in certain instances been sufficient to cause successful excavation to be carried out in promising spots.

The two genealogical tree figures which are given on page 90 alongside each other reproduce two diverse illustrations, opposing each other categorically, of the development of the Primates and of the coming of man in the course of the last world epochs. According to Weinert the development towards man was realised from the already highly specialized anthropoid apes only at the beginning of the Ice Age. The same, or similar, anatomical and physiological characteristics in chimpanzee and man (blood groups with their agglutinogenes, structure of the blood albumen) even the absence of fossil human remains before the Ice Age seemed to confirm his view. Osborn, on the other hand, wishes to erect quite a different concept for discussion with his genealogical tree (right): he argues that from beings which in the Oligocene epoch of the Tertiary period, 40 m. y. ago, were not yet either distinctly anthropoid apes or quite man-like, issued both the anthropoids (pongids) and the man-like (hominids). If the Tertiary hominids were not quite human in our

sense of the word then, according to Osborn, the humanisation in this inconceivably long time of 40 m. y. has been steadily completed. Osborn's projection of a genealogical history of the Primates had only the great disadvantage that it was pure theory for, from the Tertiary, there were certainly fossil anthropoid apes documented by finds not, however, hominids. Only Hürzeler's Oreopithecus from the upper Miocene epoch about 10 m. y. ago appeared to give some solid foundation for Osborn's working theory. If Oreopithecus was really a hominid, then the genealogical diagram of H. Weinert would not suffice to include the 10 m. y. old marsh-dweller from Tuscany in such a scheme.

Pedigree diagrams are only roughly simplified sketches which are intended to represent the basis for discussion. Behind them stands the pressing question: when did a Primate with human features detach itself from the animal relationship and from which bestial development series did beings with pure human characteristics diverge? On this there are numerous hypotheses:

1. According to the German palaeontologist, Edgar Dacque, men or man-like beings already lived in the Cretaceous period; they were contemporaries of the saurians, because our tales of dragons can only be derived from actual experience of these giant lizards.

2. The German anatomist, M. Westenhöfer, is convinced of an "individual path of man" in the

Tertiary. The human hand in its primitive form is for him, among others, a characteristic implying that man had already in the Eocene of the Tertiary gone on his isolated individual way to the exclusion of the apish Primate line.

3. The Australian zoologist, F. Wood-Jones, derives man from the same origin as the Primates, from the primitive tarsiers. Thence he went his own way. From here on the protocatarrhinan hypothesis is also to be understood. Catarrhinae (or Cercopithecoids) are the narrow-nosed monkeys of the Old World. The divergence of the human and animal paths is transferred to the phase of the Prosimiae with lemurs, loris and tarsius relations.

4. The great majority of scientists adhere to the pongid hypothesis, according to which man has not branched off either from the lemuroids or from the monkeys of the Old World. The common ancestors of men and lower apes are to be sought for in anthropoids. The adherents of the pongid hypothesis are divided into two very contradictory camps. In one stand the "antibrachiatorists" and in the other the "brachiatorists". In spite of their abstruse names the opposing views are very easy to understand.

4 a. The early - pongid hypothesis or prebrachiator hypothesis asserts that the highly specialized hanging and swinging climbers (brachiators), the present anthropoid apes with relatively long arms and comparatively short legs, could not possibly have been the forebears of the simple, still primitive palaeoanthropines and neoanthropines. All agree in the view of the evolution of organisms that an already highly specialized unilaterally adapted being, as is the brachiating ape, cannot be an ancestor of man, whose real forebears in different temporal periods have always avoided specialization. Evolution is irrevocable.

4b. The "brachiatorists", adherents of the brachiating hypothesis, add up the characteristics they have in common which connect the brachiators, particularly the chimpanzees, with recent man. The forward movement as brachiators, so they say, first induced the upright carriage, the erect walk and the freeing of the hands and at the same time caused the immense cultivation of the cranium and of the human brain.

Fig. 70. Review of the hypotheses of the roots of the anthropoid in non-human forebears, after G. Heberer. 1. Brachiator hypothesis. 2. Early pongids hypothesis. 3. Proto-Catarrhine hypotheses. P. H. T. the transition field of Anthropoid- ape-Man, AMT = Animal-Man Transition, Pr = Prehominids, Eu = True humans (Euhominines), Ar = Archanthropines, Pa = Ancient Man (Palaeonthropines), Ne (Neathropines), New Men, O = Orang Utan, G = Gorilla, P = Pan (Chimpanzee).

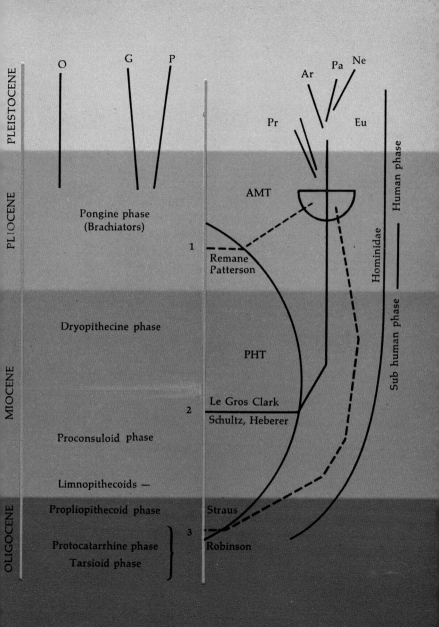

PLEISTOCENE

PLIOCENE

MIOCENE

OLIGOCENE

O   G   P

Ar   Pa Ne

Pr   Eu

AMT

Human phase

Pongine phase
(Brachiators)

Hominidae

1

Remane
Patterson

Dryopithecine phase

Sub human phase

PHT

2

Le Gros Clark

Schultz, Heberer

Proconsuloid phase

Limnopithecoids —

Propliopithecoid phase   Straus

3

Protocatarrhine phase
Tarsioid phase

Robinson

SYSTEM OF THE PRIMATES

I PROSIMII

1. Lemurs (Lemuri-
   forms)
   Examples: Cerco-
   pithecus, lemur
   mongoz, propithe-
   cus, aye aye
2. Loris (Lorisforms)
   Examples: Stenops
   tardigradus, dwarf
   galago, potto
3. Tarsier (Tarsii-
   forms)
   Example: Tarsius
   tarsius

II APES AND MAN (ANTHROPOIDEA)

1. New World or broad-
   nosed monkeys
   (Platyrrhina)
   Examples: Spider
   monkey, capuchins,
   midas monkey

2. Narrow-nosed or
   Old World monkeys
   (Catarrhina)

a) Macaques or tailed
   monkeys (Cerco-
   pithecoidea)
   Examples: Baboon,
   rhesus, mandrill,
   cercopithecus

b) Anthropoid apes
   and man (Anthropo-
   morpha or
   Hominoidea)

aa) Anthropoid apes
   (Pongidae)
   Examples: Gibbon,
   siamang, orang-
   utan, chimpanzee,
   gorilla

bb) Humans
   (Hominoidea)
   Examples: fossil
   and recent humans
   of numerous races

PRIMATES OR ANTHROPOID APES

Dentition   Heteromorphus (various)
well developed pre-molars (monkeylike)

MAN

developed pre-molars (hominid)
developd premolars (hominid)

Gibbon   Gorilla   Chimpanzee   Oreopithecus   Pekin man (Sinanthropus)   Man

Skull   Maned baboon

rang Utan   Gorilla   Chimpanzee   Oreopithecus (first attempt at reconstruction)   Rhodesian man from Broken hill, Rhodesia   Man (European)

Pelvis

Baboon (dachelada)   Chimpanzee   Oreopithecus   Australanthropus   Man

△ Fig. 72. To facilitate a systematic survey of the Primates and to show their sub orders, families and genera, this series of pictures from the Natural History Museum at Basle will be useful. They represent dentition, skull and pelvis, in that order, of tarsiers and anthropoid apes still existing today and compare them with those of fossil and recent men. In the middle are the dentition, skull and pelvis of Oreopithecus bambolii.

◁ Fig. 71. The pictures given here from the Basle Natural History Museum show the ontogenetical development of the Primates up to Man, based on types still extant today. Left to right: Tarsius, Loris (Galago), Lemur (Cerco), Black spider monkey (Ateles), Anubis baboon (Papio), Chimpanzee (Pan).

Fig. 73. In the relief map of the world the possible "primordial home" of Man is marked. The presumable centre of origin of the hominids extends over a very wide area and is bounded by: The Pamirs — Himalayas — Sunghin — East Tien-chan — Altai — Great Altai — Tarbag Atai, Ala-tau and Tien-Shan. It was only through information provided by the new fossils from geographical, geomorphological, climatological and botanogeographical sources that one of the most stirring stories of science has been rescued from an uncertain position of speculation. Critical comparisons of serious and well founded theories admit of one general fact — namely that of the geographical origin of Man. Two possible places of origin, North Africa-Europe and Africa, gave way in favour of Asia. Australia, North and South America were ruled out from the start. Only in the regions of the Old World monkeys in which pongids fossil and living are present could the original home of Man be sought. ▷

III

EMERGENCE OF THE SPIRIT

Once again, and with good reason, shall the skull of an ideal extreme classical Neandertal Man from the last Ice Age be produced. Compared to "the Old Man of La Chapelle aux Saints", the "Youth from Grimaldi" appears as a new, conquering, bright and mature type of man. However, not Age and Youth but Ancient man and New man are contrasted here with their overwhelming strength of expression which grows far beyond the merely individual. First by comparison and then placed alongside each other *both* gain in general humanity; only seen from both their points of view can one appreciate properly the new world of Homo sapiens which is now glittering and beckoning towards the future.

In 1908 the French anthropologist, Marcelin Boule, dug up an almost complete skeleton from a pit half a metre deep in the village of La Chapelle aux Saints in the South of France. The grave of the "Old Man" was covered by a "culture layer" which contained fine stone implements and the bones of rhinoceros, reindeer, bison and wild goat. The artefacts belonged to the Mousterian culture and the old man may have lived 60,000 years ago. He was the representative Neandertal Man from the beginning of the last Ice Age, as v. Eickstedt described him in so masterly a manner "mighty brow ridges,

skull as flat as a pancake, retreating chin and 'hangdog' head, thus altogether a fairly primitive, coarse, even ugly appearance of the head with a lithe and delicately boned body formation.

He however proved to be an isolated fringe phenomenon by his aberrant specializations, his large-headedness and flattened cranium, his

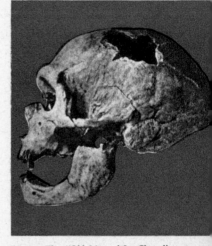

Fig. 74. The "Old Man of La Chapelle aux Saints".

sharp featured countenance, both in front and below, wide high bulbous nose and various special characteristics. With his large and lively eyes and the considerable mobility of his features to express his moods the Neandertaler must have been good tempered — cheery and merry when not roused and terrifyingly brutal if stirred and angered. And this change came about quickly, as is still so in children and primitives. The classic

Neandertaler of the beginning of the last Ice Age was thus of short growth, thickset and strong, being still not fully erect of bearing, with a very nimble and muscular form a giant skull buried in massive muscle complexes and a plump, flattish, coarse face."

On the Riviera near Mentone there are, in Italian territory, nine caves

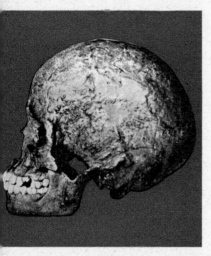

Fig. 75. The "Grimaldi Youth", left view of skull (after Aichel).

and grottos. They lie on the red-coloured coast which falls steeply to the Mediterranean and were investigated from 1872 to the end of the century. In one of the grottos near Grimaldi was found the skeleton of an elderly woman, together with that of a young man. In the skull of the "Youth of Grimaldi" we meet "modern" Homo sapiens. During an Interglacial spell in the climate in the last Ice Age, approximately 45,000

years ago, there appeared in many parts of the world from South Africa to China, Japan and Australia these new men, the Neanthropines. The man of the late Palaeolithic who unfolded apparently so explosively in the shattering mirror image of our own bodily composition: he possesses the profile countenance of Europeans, his steeply rising brow is marvellously domed. The narrow skull, the small orbital cavity, the narrow nose, the finely formed lower jaw, the distinct forward thrust of the chin are only slightly different from the normal Homo sapiens, modern man. What bodily strength and spiritual power contributed to make this Grimaldi youth with the appearance which he now presents to us — this can be elucidated for us best by one of the biggest adventures of Homo sapiens diluvialis: the conquering of America by an old stratum of Homo sapiens, from which the Grimaldi race must have issued (the so-called Brünn race, the Aurignacians and the Cromagnon Men also). It is commonly believed that only at the end of the Ice Age had differentiated races of the Mongoloids been driven forth to America. It may, however, be believed that even before the formation of races by Homo sapiens, before a Homo sapiens at all, a people came forth out of central Asia and crossed over the Bering strait to form the Amerindian races; so that long before the post-glacial period a non-American-Indian pre-Sapiens man had spread over the whole American continent.

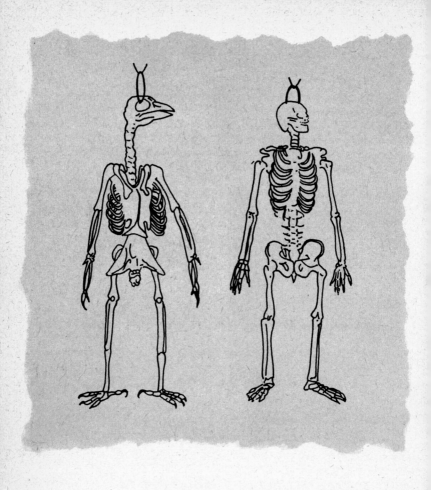

Fig. 76. At the end of the survey of the fossil men and their forebears which provides a biological-scientific picture of the origin of man it must be borne in mind that the recognition of the relationship of living beings towards each other is at least four hundred years old. The French zoologist, Belon, published in 1555 his „Histoire de la nature des oiseaux" in which he showed a picture of two skeletons, one of a bird and the other human. He had it drawn from mounted specimens which in those days were kept in curio show-cases. Belon saw that Man was closely connected with the animals; he carried out morphological studies as early as that. With this investigation of the original picture (which Goethe first called morphology) Belon wished to show that the hand and arm of man correspond to the wing of a bird, that therefore "Man belongs to Nature" as Goethe expressed it. So Belon probably knew 400 years ago that man did not issue complete from the hands of his Maker but that he carried his own plan as an animal, and after which he was built, and his nature, within himself.

The beginning of the last North American Wisconsin Ice Age was determined by analyses of deep sea bore cores to have been 70,000 years ago, after the last Interglacial, which in America is called the Sargamon, had come to an end. Whilst clay in the Sandia Cave in La Huerta Cañon in New Mexico was being examined, a new Interglacial was recognised besides the Sargamon. It had interrupted the Wisconsin Ice Age for a period of several thousand years, 40,000 years ago. In this nearly 50,000 year old clay layer were found spear heads and the remains of game. The men who must have used them had killed species now long extinct, wild horses, camels, mastodons, elephants and bisons. The people of the Sandia culture had already at least 40,000 years before covered the enormous distance from East Asia over the Bering Strait to New Mexico.

The migrations became confusing and more extraordinary when human skeletal remains, which had been found near Vero and Melbourne on the East Coast of Florida as long ago as 1916, were re-examined by nuclear physical and geological investigations in attempts to rearrange them. If the dating agrees, then those representatives of an ancient stratum of Homo sapiens had immigrated before the Sandia people in the Interglacial Sargamon 70,000 years ago and thus become, so far, the most ancient "Americans". They also could have come only from Asia and must have used the then land bridge across the present Bering Strait to reach Florida after having followed the Missouri and Mississippi. It is certain beyond doubt that American man had not developed on the American continent but had immigrated from North East or East Asia. The comparison of palaeo-American finds (not palaeo-Indian, for the American Indians are not the successors of the ancient first immigrants) with the relics of old human cultures of the Atlantic coasts of Africa and Europe completely excluded that perhaps mythical seafarers crossed the ocean at that time and discovered the New World.

Besides the evidence from the Sandia cave there were found in Texas oven pits of the elephant hunters. With the discovery of other finds on the high plateau of the Llano Estacado they were collected together into the Llano-culture. The fourteen hearth pits near Lewisville in Denton County with charred bones and stone tips from throwing weapons were more than 37,000 years old. The bill of fare of these Llano people consisted not only of the flesh of mammoths, it was so varied and rich that the hunters must have lived in a veritable paradise. The meals consisted of elephant, bison, camel, wild horse, giant armadillo, antelope, bear, deer, wolf, coyote, prairie dog, badger, washbear, skunk, rabbit, field rat, field mouse, birds, swamp turtle, grass snake, fresh water snails, mussels, a mason bee nest with larvae, and finally of the seeds of the Celtis occidentalis tree. Perhaps simultaneously with the Sandia and Llano cultures, there were traces of man found on the island of Santa Rosa off the coast of California. The island is in a group which now lies 45 km from the land. The channel which separates the islands from the mainland is now about 215 m. deep. It could not have dried even during the height of the last glaciation. Since, however, mammals lived at Santa Rosa at least 37,000 years ago they must have wandered there by

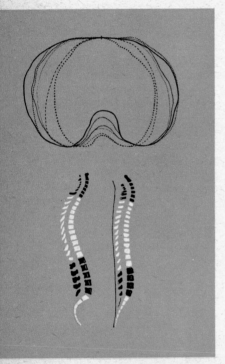

some primeval land bridge. They had, because of their isolation, developed differently to their relations.

The people themselves, whose many cultural layers were superim-

Fig. 77. On pages 35 to 44 the physical characteristics of man are detailed, they make him akin to animals and through them he is also clearly distinguished from the beasts. First the erect carriage made the high differentiation of his brain possible ontogenetically; the cerebrum quickly enlarged thereafter. Before turning to the spiritual development of man we point again to two important characters confined to mankind — the development of the vertebral column and thorax.

In the illustration we compare (below) the vertebral column of a man (left) with that of a chimpanzee (after v. Eickstedt). Appropriately bent it receives the shocks of a bipedal, quick footed man and absorbs them; equally elastically it carries the long-necked head.

The upper illustration shows the outlines of the chest (thorax) of a macaque (macaca, a catarrhine monkey) and man. The comparitive picture clarifies the development up to the wide and flat human chest so necessary for an upright attitude. The spinal column clings to the thorax and has literally grown into it — thus supporting the organs of the chest (after v. Eickstedt).

These purely human traits are the necessary preliminaries to a cephalization (an increase of brain).

◁

Fig. 78. An "arteriogram" of a human brain. The Portuguese physician, E. Moniz, elaborated a process in 1927 for the X-ray examination of the vascular system especially of the arteries, into which he squirted his contrast fluid. This "Vasography" was later extended so that by injecting a contrasting fluid into the inner carotid artery the brain vessels could be distinguished in the X-ray picture. In this picture the fore and middle cerebral arteries are made visible A) the inner cephalic artery, B) the injection needle.

This arteriogram of a living man is an incomparable documentation of the organ that made Homo sapiens the Lord of the earth, but also made him the most dangerous mammal. There repose in him overpowering human talents, an immense power of memory, an awareness of himself and his environment, the most intimate connection between doing (practice) and knowledge (gnosis), which perhaps is centred in the gyrus (brain convolution) supramarginalis in the left lower temporal convolution, in which the centre of speech is also concealed. ▷

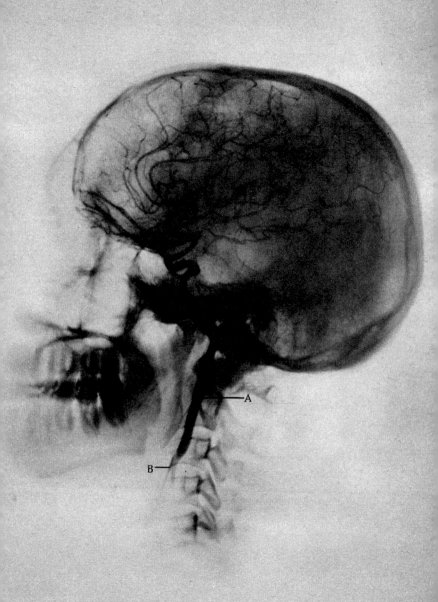

posed one upon another, may have colonised Santa Rosa 30,000 years ago. The radio-carbon method of determination showed the age of the first and lowest layer camp at 29,650 years. How man reached the island remains a mystery. Either he bridged the open channel with boats or else the island still formed a part of the mainland.

In 1958 stone artefacts were found on the coast of Alaska *below* a culture-free layer of several metres thickness. This sterile sedimentary cover represented the sedimentation of an ancient sea in which were found small marine organisms, the shells of diatoms which can live only in a depth of sea water of less than 70 m. The primeval colonisation region had been flooded later by the sea which must have been at least 70 m deep, a sea which must have been formed in one of the warm periods 40,000 or 70,000 years ago. In 1954 at Thule Springs on the banks of a former river in the present desert of southerly Nevada, the dwelling of an ancient camel hunter was laid bare. The carbon time scale showed an age of 24,000 years, the then limit of the method. Geologists estimated the age of the prehistoric camp at double that age. In all these camp sites, dwellings, hearth fires and colonies the remains of stone weapons and game were found but not human

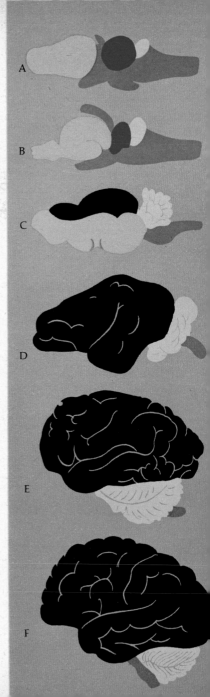

Fig. 79. The cerebral cortex with its folds in man and beast. From above downward: A fish, B amphibian, C reptile, D Tarsius, E anthropoid ape, F man (A to E after Portmann, F after Scharrer).

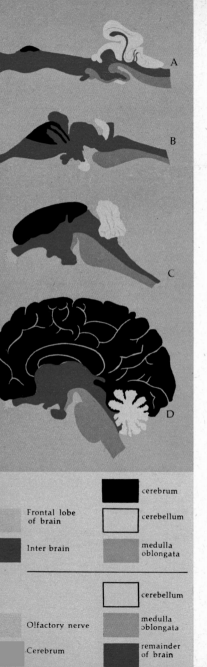

	cerebrum
Frontal lobe of brain	cerebellum
Inter brain	medulla oblongata

	cerebellum
Olfactory nerve	medulla oblongata
Cerebrum	remainder of brain

skeletal remains — if one regards the human remains at Vero and Melbourne in Florida as not determined with certainty in their estimated age. Apart from that, the human skull unearthed by H. de Terra in 1947 in the basin of Mexico City still counts as the oldest human find hitherto in the American Continent. This "Tepexpan Man" was a Mongoloid type called the "generalized Mongoloid". Thus he did not yet belong to the Mongoloids of extreme form of the far North, the Tunguses or Eskimo, with definite slanting eyes and sunken nose roots.

Finds in East Brazil, South Brazil and Ecuador also lead to the conclusion that they were men with as yet little difference from ancient European characteristics, which probably were taken over from the oldest immigrants before the splitting up of Homo sapiens into differentiated races, before the Palaeo-Indians and also before the "Folsom-culture", whose sites lay above the Llano layers. The Folsom bison-hunters may well have crossed the Bering Strait only after the end of the last Ice Age but did not, like their forefathers, fifty thousand years earlier, follow the North American West Coast but streamed along the Yukon and colonised, besides the

Fig. 80. Development of the brain of vertebrates (after Edinger) compared with the brain of man. The cerebrum is blackened. Whereas the other here variously coloured parts of the brain are comparatively well developed also in the shark (A), in the lizard (B) and in the rabbit (C), the human development in the cerebrum (D) easily takes first place.

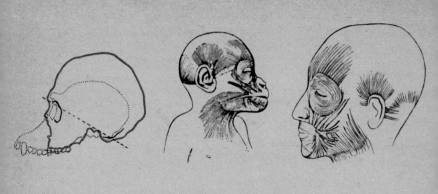

Fig. 81. The proportion of cranium to facial skull in Man and chimpanzee shown on the left. In the middle and right the musculature of the head and of the face of a young chimpanzee and a man (after Huber and Loth).

Western plains, also the Eastern portions of the New World.

On such grandiose wanderings man grew to be a true man, physically and spiritually. But how he became a spiritual being is, besides the fossil history of man, the often impenetrable part of an investigation into his origin and existence. Thus the difference between man and the great apes is not required so much by corporal characteristics but lies chiefly on the biologically inconceivable side of the spirit. Yet the shape of the cranium and skull in ape and man can show proofs which allow of conclusions on the development of the spirit. Fossil finds can be of high importance for a genealogical history of the psyche and it is a fortunate circumstance that in all skeletal remains the head is the best preserved. A comparison of brain pan and facial skull of the ape with that of a man hardly needs explanation, so convincing is the

heightened skull cap of Homo sapiens. It surveys the earth, in the truest sense of the word — without snout or brow ridge which have vanished. Just as impressive is the comparison of the musculature of the head and of the face of a young chimpanzee with that of a man. The cephalic cap of muscle has in Homo sapiens recens completely disappeared. Since man no longer seizes with the jaws of the snout, the apish heavy strands of muscle about the mouth parts have given place to a high muscle differentiation — thus man gained in facial expression. Besides the musculature of man's cheeks and mouth regions expresses the most important change: man has become a speaking creature. To see himself and his like contrasted with all other things and organisms, to stand back from the world and finally to regard himself as an object amongst the many other things and living beings in his ambient — that only man can do. His

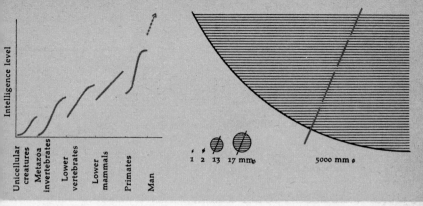

Fig. 82. In the left hand figure the level of intelligence is estimated. On the right the "delayed action" is shown as a feat of memory in the form of spheres and their volume for: lemur, New World monkeys, Old World monkeys, anthropoid apes and Man (after Nissen and Fischel).

soul does not rank higher than that of animals; each animal and perhaps each plant has a soul. But only man possesses mind because his brain can store infinitely more impressions and knows how to connect the most diverse things and impressions of things as no beast may. Memory and intelligence (to learn from experience) has reached in man in the course of the ontogenesis of the organisms a preliminary zenith. This high point, however, does not mean a departure from nature. Our relationship with the beasts is preserved.

Biology can nevertheless only reach one dimension of the human spirit. Here is an example: the memory of animals only serves the fulfilment of their urgent desires. If the desired goal of the urge moves into the animal's vicinity without it being accessible at the moment it will retain prey or titbit in mind as well as its habitat in memory and

defer its activities against the prey. This "deferred action" is a performance of the memory. The tarsius can remember for perhaps 5 seconds, the gibbon 15 seconds and the large apes 2 hours. But the human memory knows no bounds.

Man needs, for the development of his individual brain, over nine months, for even in the suckling and in childhood the brain continues to grow since it is not yet ready. In this germination the simple ground plans from which the brain was developed during human pre-history repeat themselves. The evolutionary historical brain evolution lasted for hundreds of millions of years, for man received his brain, and particularly his richly convoluted cerebrum, not without the help of his more simply fashioned forebears. The course of the development of the brain through this entire genealogical history can today still be follow-

Species	Weight of brain in grammes	Weight of brain / to weight of body	Comparative value
1. Man	1375	1 : 30	35
2. Chimpanzee	400	1 : 75	5.2
3. Orang utan	400	1 : 124	3
4. Gorilla	425	1 : 231	2
5. Horse	520	1 : 534	0.97
6. Blue whale	7000	1 : 15,000	0.47
7. Dog	102	1 : 250	0.37
8. Cat	32	1 : 128	0.25
9. Sparrow	0.84	1 : 29	0.029
10. Ostrich	29	1 : 1200	0.024
11. Pigeon	1.9	1 : 152	0.013
12. Chicken	3.4	1 : 446	0.007

Fig. 83. To compare the vertebrata with man, to determine their degree of development and their position in the zoological system, one might weigh the brains. But an exact comparison of the weight of the brain without consideration of the various sizes of body leads to no classification of the animals by their level of rank, for the brain of a dove weighs, for instance, two grammes and that of a blue whale fourteen pounds. The naturalist Cuvier as long ago as 1805 examined the relationship between weight of brain and body weight in vertebrates. From the figures he got, which were independent of the weight of body, the level of rank of living beings could not be determined. R. Anthony, Portmann and K. Wirz found useful, though very difficult methods with which the level of vertebrates could be determined by means of their brains. H. Malthaner started recently, in a simple manner, a "comparable value", a "comparable" size which is obtained by squaring the value of the weight of brain and dividing by the body-weight. According to Cuvier's proportional figures the sparrow stands above man and the whale would be far below the birds. In the examples quoted in the table which takes its order from the comparable value, man sensibly occupies first place.

ed in living animals. And in this the development history of the cerebrum is the most important. Only through the specialized development and greatly varied articulation of the cerebrum has man emerged after beginning to remain erect and using his hands with such skill, it was this organ which decided on his spirit, on his capability to deal with things and at the same time to learn to recognise his dealings as such. Only in Tarsius tarsius is there a beginning of a convoluted surface of the cerebrum to be seen. The cerebral pallium with its convolutions (gyri) and its furrows (sulci) could only find room in a folded state inside the cranium and only with the help of this manifold articulation did man cross the Rubicon of the spirit. If, indeed, tarsius and anthropoid ape show these foldings, yet it is the "grey cortex" of man, with its area of $200,000 \, mm^2$, which is the highest brain specialization among all organisms and the only tangible unilateral adaptation of the erect hairless Primates.

It should be remarked at this point, however, that during the process of humanisation it was not the total size of the brain which was decisive. The French palaeontologist Boule, measured the volume of the brain of the Neandertal Man of La Chapelle aux Saints and determined a brain capacity of 1,620 ccm whilst recent man shows only 1,500 ccm. The Neandertaler of Spy in Belgium actually showed a capacity of 1,723 ccm. When Boule received this sensational result he was so afraid of the amount that he lacked the courage to publish it. It is now certain that Ice Age man far surpassed the present male European in size of brain — from this it must be concluded that the performance of the brain has nothing to do with its size, only the folding, the rich, manifold articulation, the height of the cerebral differentiation decides the power of memory and the level of intelligence.

The physician and anatomist, F. J. Gall, in the last century doubted the unity of the soul. He dissected the life of the soul into a great number of different "soul potentialities", such as courage, love of children or sense of theft, which he pinned down to certain spots in the brain. The brain anatomist, Flechsig, announced in 1894 "that the brain as an organ covers the soul's phenomena fully and entirely and that we are capable of developing its requirements to a clarity equal to everything else accessible to our comprehension which is happening naturally". This radical atomisation of the only metaphysically comprehensible soul has survived in part until today. In charts of the brain certain psychic and bodily processes are placed in relation to spe-cial regions of the brain; body, soul and spirit are localised diagrammatically in certain parts of the brain, and thus projected on to the surface of the brain. It is not possible, however, to insert individual functions of man rigidly into regions of the brain. Such projections of the soul, of the spirit and of the body on a brain chart suffice for a limited practice of the nerve specialist and the brain surgeon for damage, dilatation and for specific diagnoses of cerebral tumours. Certainly, in certain maladies of the brain, soul and spirit in man may be changed — equally well can one, however, also remove regions of the cerebral cortex in man and beast, without the memory and behaviour being influenced. The brain is not a collection of parts but a living organ working as a whole and forming with the central nervous system an indivisible entity. Soul and spirit are inextricably interwoven and are not to be isolated as individual functions into sections. Finally, topographical maps of the brain and brain pathology can never discover a "seat of the soul". One cannot dissociate body, soul and spirit from one another. Before all investigation body, soul and spirit should never be sundered. It should be realized that from the skeletal remains of fossil men only his bodily circumstances can be deduced. The spirit has fled from the petrified remains; the feeling, experiencing, knowing, thinking of the early men have faded away; the possibilities of his dealings and his soul's ways of

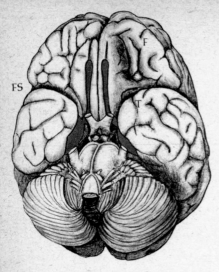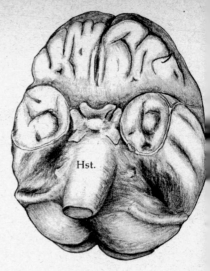

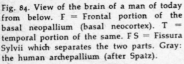

Fig. 84. View of the brain of a man of today from below. F = Frontal portion of the basal neopallium (basal neocortex). T = temporal portion of the same. F S = Fissura Sylvii which separates the two parts. Gray: the human archepallium (after Spatz).

Fig. 85. Endocrane cast of the cranium of a male individual. The positive of the impressions of the convolutions at the inner surface of the skull correspond to the convolutions of the brain of the basal neocortex (compare fig. 84). The relief of the condex cerebri (Hst) of the archepallium and the neighbouring rear section of the frontal brain do not appear for they do not impress themselves on the inner side of the skull (after Spatz).

Fig. 86. Cast of cranium (endocrane) of fossil Homo rhodesiensis in the same position. Comparatively poor impressions of both portions of the basal neocortex (compare fig. 85). Gray: defects of the skull (after Spatz).

behaviour can never be reconstructed from the bony remains. One must always draw conclusions from the results of animal and child psychology to understand the psyche of the primeval man — apart, always, from the few cultural heirlooms. The only and deep nucleus of the becoming of man, namely the spiritual upsurge in the human sphere of the consciousness and knowledge of self is for us closed for ever.

Here, however, new and astonishing investigations by the German Professor, H. Spatz, take a hand, they make use of scientific methods to at least throw new light, from the physical point of view, on the origin of man and on his future. As the illustrations on this page show, the convolutions of the cerebrum can be made out from the fossilized skulls where they have "imprinted" themselves on the inside of the skull — and more especially the manifold articulation of the cerebrum, its differentiations, which are expressed in the impressions on fossil skulls, can make decisive witnesses to the genealogical historical development of the human spirit. In the Postscript to this book "The future man" further detailed information will be given on this subject. Early Homo sapiens diluvialis, was 40,000 years

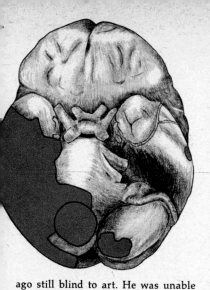

ago still blind to art. He was unable to express his beliefs, his experiences, his worship of the unknown and incomprehensible in rock paintings, engravings or small plastic figures. But other proofs of his magic and rich internal world give notice how he analysed the secrets of life and death spiritually. What lay hidden behind his bulging brow can be read partly from his bequests. Upper Palaeolithic Man already disposed of a differentiated social concept. His handiness, his tradition and teaching brought him culturally to a very high stage. Of this we have indications. Ceremonial burials and cults of the bear, for instance, were widely distributed long before Aurignacian times, before the creative, artistic activity of man in Europe — they bear witness to a deep spiritual world of early man.

As in the Drachenloch cave (see Fig. 89) so also in other Alpine caverns at approximately, 2,000 m.

height, similar cult sites existed with hearths, stone tables and chests in which the skulls of "Brother Bear" were coffined. In the bear religion of these pre-Neandertalers the cave-bear was honoured like a god and sacrificed for his strength and likeness to man. He was literally domesticated, kept in captivity, cared for, and loved; as to this day tribes in Northern Siberia bring up bears and treat them as part of the family until the time of sacrifice comes round. These early men lived in the dark of the incomprehensible, in "Mana" still, in the trembling awe of Beings and Things which carried power in themselves. The cave-bear, the "strong as a bear" was such an individual endowed with might, who was sacrificed to the incomprehensible. Palaeolithic Man was cult-ridden and one may be sure that ruling priests emerged from his tribes, hordes and families who, as shamans and witch-doctors, with their outstanding ability, guided the cults.

In the Aurignacian Age during the warm climatic fluctuation of the last Ice Age there came about the decisive turn: the Middle Palaeolithic almost leapt into the upper Palaeolithic. And it was in the upper Palaeolithic that for the first time man gave expression to his beliefs, his feelings and thoughts with figurines, engravings and exorcist rock-paintings.

In the valley of the La Sagne rivulet near the town of Cahors (in the French Departement of Lot) lie the caves of Pech Merle, amongst

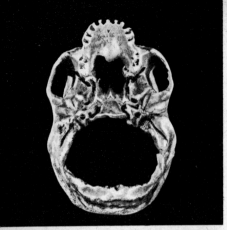

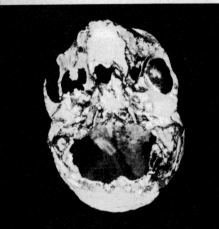

which is one of the same name. It contains the artistic creations of the early Aurignacians. Among them are traces of fingers which were pressed in the clay of the cave roof some 40,000 years ago. Through the irregularly crossing lines, which are called "maccaronis", there are distinguishable the outlines of a woman with large pendulous breasts. From the carelessly thrown-off lines it was concluded that all rock painting had had its beginning with that. From a childish groping there would gradually emerge art, which slowly and little by little found always higher forms up to the master workers of the Magdalenian "Art for Art's sake" ("l'art pour l'art"). This is quite un-

Fig. 87. The skull of a "classical" Neandertal Man from Monte Circeo (Italy) compared with a Melanesian's skull. Here is the same sort of enlargement of the base of the skull for the removal of the brain. The skull of the Neandertaler had been ceremoniously interred. "One could believe", so wrote Prof. Gieseler of this illustration "that there are here the marks of an old custom in which skull enlargement for the purpose of removing the brain had been handed down from generation to generation for millennia. That it is not a tradition passed over from our European Neandertalers is obvious because of the distance, quite apart from the historical position of the Neandertal Man in which we assume that in Europe they had died out without descendants." The lesson to be learnt is: homicide and cannibalism do not exclude the ceremonial burying of heads, and a skull cult.

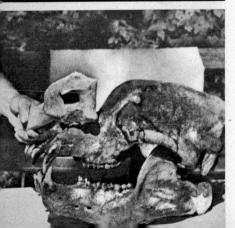

Fig. 88. This makes clear in what manner the captive cave bear was killed before a "bear feast". In the Salzofen cave, near Bad Aussee, skeletons of skulls of bears and tools have been found from which this "sacrifical slaugther" can be reconstructed.

proved and also unlikely. The perceptive thinking, the circle of experience of the Aurignacians, their magic world, their imaginative outlook, which was riddled with religion and shackled by it, has nothing to do with our spiritual attitude and with our execution of art. We can never quite penetrate the secrets of the people of 40,000 years ago. Besides, there is no doubt that the pictures in the Aurignacian period came to maturity

the mountain of El Castillo. Even the pre-Neandertalers during the Interglacial before the last Ice Age would have regarded it with awed veneration. It is riddled with a mighty cave system of halls, galleries and passages, which have names like El Castillo, La Pasiega, Cueva de las Monedas and Cueva de las Chimeneas. This subterranean world was one of the oldest cult sites of mankind and remained so for uncounted

Fig. 89. Cross section of a cult site from the last Interglacial period about 80,000 years ago (after Kraft). In high-lying Alpine caves the oldest cult sites on earth have been found. The picture shows the sequence of strata in the Drachenloch cave with A) heaped up bear's bones behind a stone wall, B) a covered hearth and C) careful burial of the skulls of the cave-bear (Ursus spelaeus).

immediately and that there had been no primitive predecessors to this "art". The traces of drawing fingers, the "maccaronis" might equally well be traces of an absent-mindedly moving hand which had just before executed a complete picture.

In the Spanish Province of Santander there lies, near Puente Viesgo,

generations of Stone Age hunters and for millennia. In a vast series of strata the heritage of entire nations of prehistory have been found. In the depth of the caverns of Monte Castillo the powers of experience are still awake, which brought to expression their beliefs and their worship in times which

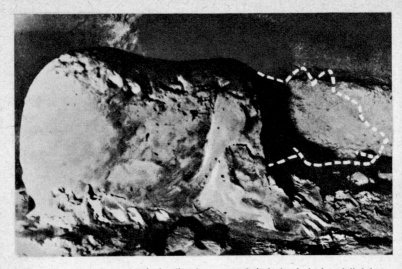

Fig. 90. Shows the cult picture of a headless bear upon which the head of a bear killed during cult celebrations was placed.

comprise a period ten times as long as our own historical times. The walls of the Castillo cave are covered with cult pictures, exorcising symbols and magic hunting rites in the form of game of all kinds, but some covered with mysterious signs and dots. Behind the hall of "Bison and Stalagmites" next to the "Gallery of the Elephants" lies the "Gallery of Hand Impressions" from which comes the "hand negative" illustrated here. Man of the Palaeolithic age pressed his affirming hand on the rock and squirted the outlines with red pigment. So the "hand negative" remained fixed on the cave wall — perhaps that of a priest, shaman and magician — forever begging, admonishing or as an expression of his self-confidence, and today it

remains as freh and alive as it was 40,000 years ago.

In the artistic creative force of men of the more recent Palaeolithic age the cave of "Three brothers" (Trois frères) near Montes-Quieu Avantès at the northern fringe of the Pyrenees, acquired an outstand-

Fig. 91. The skeleton of an elderly woman and that of a young man from the Grimaldi grottos (after the family name of the Prince of Monaco) near Mentone. In one cave were found in 1874/75 nearly three metres below the surface two children's skeletons. This "Children's Grotto" contained a succession of layers of 10 m thickness which harboured still further complete human skeletons: somewhat above the children the skeleton of an elderly woman, at a depth of 7 m the skeleton of a man 1.90 m tall whose hands had been placed folded on his breast, and lastly, in the lowest layer, the skeletons shown here. They were found in a crouching position close together.

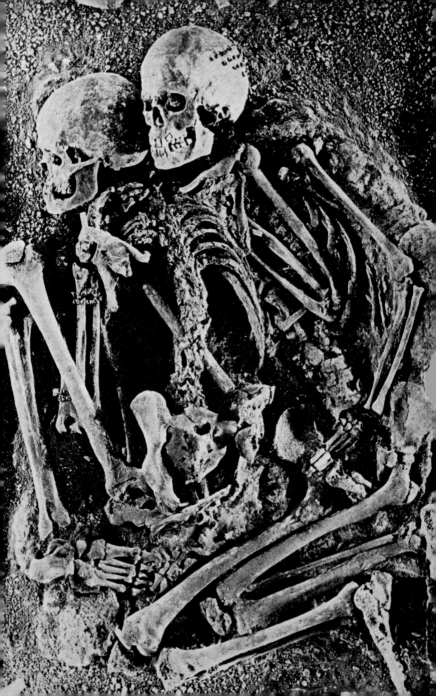

Fig. 93. The "Magician" from the Trois Frères cave at the northern rim of the Pyrenees. He is much more universally known as the "Oldest human portrait" (fig. 99). This rock picture may be said to have won world renown.

ing position, particularly because of the figure of a dancing magician or priest in the "Sanctuary", a sort of rough chapel at the outer end of the cave system. The figure, masked by reindeer antlers, reindeer ears, owls' mask, bear's paws, wild horses' tails and the genitalia of a wild cat, looks at the observer with face turned to the front, from placidly wondering, but repelling and fright-

Fig. 92. The imprint "negative" of a hand of Ice Age man in El Castillo cave in the province of Santander in Spain.

ful eyes. Four metres below him, the rock wall is covered with engravings of bisons, mammoths, rhinoceros, reindeer and mythical beings. It looks as if the magician is enthroned as the creator of the fertile animal world and master over all living things and to exorcise evil with his dance and call forth by unfathomable chance the aptitude to seize the luck of the chase. At the same time, this monstrous picture is a kind of demonstration of a well developed power of speech. For the

117

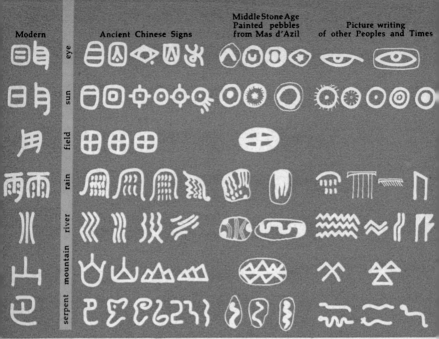

Modern		Ancient Chinese Signs	Middle Stone Age Painted pebbles from Mas d'Azil	Picture writing of other Peoples and Times
	eye			
	sun			
	field			
	rain			
	river			
	mountain			
	serpent			

Fig. 94. Picture writing (pictography) of several peoples and times compared to the painted flints from the cave tunnel at Mas-d'Azil which came from men of the Meso-lithic of the Azilian period about 10,000 years ago. The surprising similarity to pic-ture signs from other lands and later times are quite astonishing. Are there "original forms" the common heritage of humanity? This is a question which must remain open. Very bold, improved speculations and hypo-theses are often attached to the archetype (the first moulded). Here are pictographs of various peoples and times compared to Stone Age figures and signs. The prehistoric calli-graphy or pictographs were written in rock caves like that near Ronda in Southern Spain named "La Pileta". These stylized symbols were scratched by men of the Neo-lithic or late Stone Age 6,000 years ago on the rock walls to keep off animals, men and natural forces and to exorcise them. The relationship of these expressive signs with old picture signs from other parts of the world and from different times is mysterious and wonderful — but perhaps only similar in outer form by chance with a completely different meaning.

conscious change of a human being into a fabulous animal creature, the combination of various animal characteristics, the exorcising dance, the "brotherhood of nature" which is so "speakingly" expressed pre-suppose sacrifices, oracles, totems and taboos — that is, a complicated sequence of rites which can only be mastered with a good means of communication by speech.

The entire artistic creations of Palaeolithic Man form an entity which began 40,000 years ago positi-vely explosively and with complete maturity and connoisseurship, and which came to an end with the end of the Ice Age, probably under the

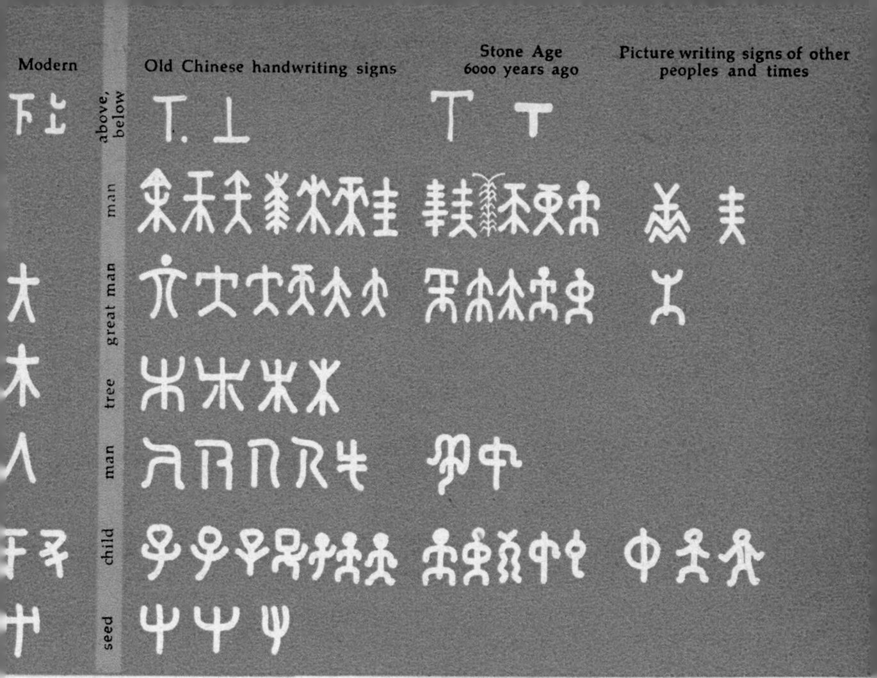

Modern		Old Chinese handwriting signs	Stone Age 6000 years ago	Picture writing signs of other peoples and times
	above, below			
	man			
	great man			
	tree			
	man			
	child			
	seed			

influence of a fundamental alteration in the conditions of life.

Side by side with the extensive time of about thirty thousand years there was also the spatial distribution of the picture creations of man with his plastic figurines, engravings and rock paintings: the will to find expression was alive from the Franco-Cantabrian area as far as Siberia, from the Mediterranean region to Africa. If he can be called an entity, he is yet divided by two spiritual areas of tension which relieved each other. In the first cultural phase of the Aurignacian-Périgordian (called after the places of discovery Aurignac and Périgord) man, and particularly the female, stood in the forefront as a theme. In the second phase of the culture in the Solutrean-Magdalenian, the animal as prey for the hunter was the ruling subject of all pictorial likenesses. With them, two quite distinct human spheres and human cultures are apparent: at the beginning of the creative departure and break-through there stood at the centre marriage and propagation. With the second stage of the last Ice Age, hunting and the hunter were the central point of a social order which realised a thorough domination by the male, in fact, a patriarchate.

Fig. 95. The Venus of Willendorf (p. 120 top), 11 cm high, from Lower Austria. ▷

Fig. 96. The ivory Venus of Lespugue (Garonne) 14.7 cm high (see p. 120 below). ▷

Fig. 97. The Venus of Savignano (Modena) made of serpentine stone. 22 cm high. ▷

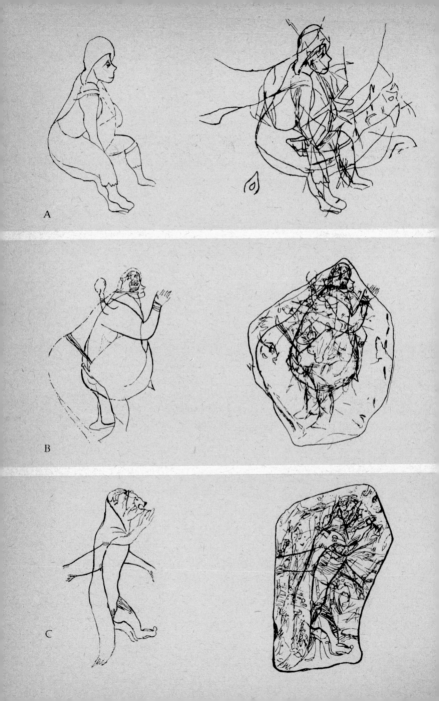

A

B

C

The cult of the mother, cults of propagation and fertility — and very likely a matriarchal social concept — are expressed in the pictures of the Aurignacian-Périgordian.

Thus, in the "Grotte du Pape" near Brassempouy (Landes) in France a single head of ivory was found only three and one half centimetres high, which certainly at one time had been part of a whole figurine. The figure has come down to us in only a fragmentary form, yet the originally powerful creation is still quite alive. The completeness of the expression and the treatment of the material makes one forget the wear of time. This picture certainly did not reproduce a realistic portrait of some individual woman — it is rather a reproduction of a moon goddess or of a divine vitalizing fertility figure. A torso which has also become famous by its beauty from the "Grotte du Pape" leads naturally to the "Venus statuettes" which have become universally known and are shown in our illustration. Here, as in those, the over-emphasis of the female characteristics, the elaboration of the fleshy parts and of the sex of the figurines show them to be idols of motherhood and fertility cults. With this maturity of constructive, creative power the

Aurignacian began at once. Apparently out of nothing and without any previous stages these extraordinary works of art appear. The Venus of Willendorf was found in a deposit of loess in the vicinity of Krems in Lower Austria. At the time of the discovery traces of red ochre colour (symbol for blood and life) still clung to the perfectly preserved figure. It belongs to the greatest creations in artistic expression of the more recent Palaeolithic. The limestone figure is executed with high skill and deep sensitiveness as a symbol of the cult of the "Great Mother". Intentionally, the characteristics of overflowing femininity with excessive fullness of body as a token of all that is womanly have been represented. Sex and propagation in this symbolic form should, of course, exceed human proportions. In the glorification of the "Great Mother" the erotic has not crept in, also the proportions have been preserved in the overemphasis. With devotion and veneration the super-human fertility was celebrated in its human mask. The Venus statuette of Savignano (Fig. 97) and the Venus of Lespugue radiate a belief and a world intelligence which reflect at the same time the social customs of the people who created these figures: the earthbound matriarchal community which finds its counterpart in a maternally minded heavenly order. Nevertheless, the Venus figures of Savignano and Lespugue are still further removed from the reproduction of the human

Fig. 98 A and B. Saucer sized scratches on limestone slabs with the figures of corpulent women from the cave at La Marche, French Dep. of Vienne.

Fig. 98 C. Shows a magician as a "bear man". The engravings belong to the Magdalenian culture.

likeness to the motherhood idol than is the Venus statuette of Willendorf. There are only indications of the physical characteristics of mankind, they are already projected far into a realm in which the human and the magical blend.

How very differently do the almost accidental and in the original almost indistinguishable scratches on a limestone slab from the cave at La Marche appear. They come from the Magdalenian, that is from the time in which the grandiose animal frescos in the rock caves of France and Spain attained the peak of their expression. Until recently it was not believed that this age of hunters had succeeded in reproducing people or even self-portraits. Animals which could be depicted with new tools, were the focus of all portraits. The pictures from this age round about 20,000 years ago, were dedicated to the magic of the chase alone, the propagation of the animals, the representation of traps, the veneration and exorcism of pregnant animals and the magical rites connected with the capture and killing of game.

Now we encounter from La Marche the precisely dated stone engravings from whose often tangled lines and superscriptions strange female figures separate themselves; rough,

naturalistically drawn, full-bodied, clad female figures for which apparently individual people have sat or stood as models. These crude portraits, which reproduce the subject of the picture's exact characteristics, where each individual characteristic is drawn in with painful accuracy, are in their coarse naturalism far from the wonderful sensitive pictures of the Venus statuettes — for there the sanctity and veneration of the "Great Mother" and often the everlasting fertile life found its purest expression.

How then did the spirit of the times change in the course of 15,000 or 20,000 years? Before agriculture and hunting confronted each other, when man, in fact had not yet become a husbandman, did not grow any plants or breed them, before, in short, a second matriarchy had been established, which remembered only the age-old mother culture — the hunters as the ruling sex had cultivated the patriarchate. With the patriarchate, the possession of game and wife was connected, the cult of the matriarchate was extinguished. From the lordly, proud self-confidence of the roaming power-possessing hunters grew the overwhelming rock paintings, engravings and figurines, in which the animal is the principal theme. The unfathomable magician of Trois Frères was dead. A new spirit had pervaded man. And in the midst of the vogue of large picture creation of the Magdalenian period there appear these scratched drawings, the size of a hand, on lime-

Fig. 99. One of the most ancient human images is this 40 cm high plastic figurine from the Louis Taillebourg cave from the village of Angles sur l'Anglin in the French Dep. of Vienne. It contains the remains of a relief frieze with representations of beasts and men of the Palaeolithic (after Zotz).

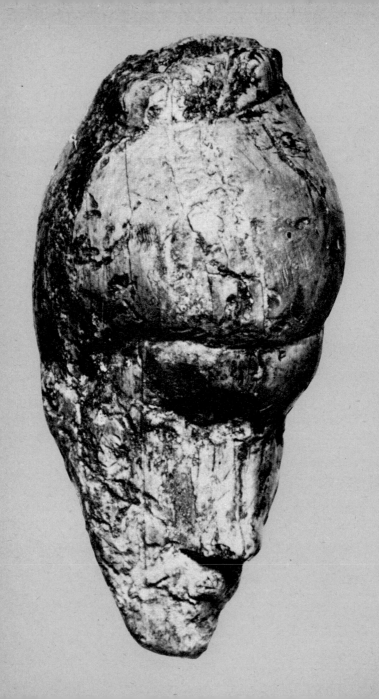

stone slabs which can only with great labour be solved to learn their rough contents: bloated, fat women in garments which are held up by bearers and with a shoulder band, in trousers which were fringed and reached to the calf, with winged caps and bracelets and knee rings. Count Vojffy, who attempted to explain the Ice Age pictures, believes he sees in these figurines, givers of milk which were kept like domestic animals as human milch cows (lactation women).

Another engraving, also from the cave at La Marche (Fig. 98 C) shows, after the "deciphering" of the original, a magician or shaman in a bear skin who allows the bear, which has been killed by spears, to rise again during his ceremonial dance — a custom which from Palaeolithic times until today has been preserved in Northern Siberia.

In Dolni Vestoniçe (Unter-Wisternitz) in Southern Moravia a mammoth-hunting station dating from the late Aurignacian was discovered in 1922 at the foot of the Pollauer mountains.

To the astonishment of the searchers, one could also trace the outlines of huts. It was, in fact, incredible that the roving hunters should have founded a village community. But there were found in California also, in Owens Valley,

proper houses; community buildings, a village colony even before the introduction of agriculture and thus a sedentary life in a hunters and collectors existence. Even if it existed in North America only 10,000 years before our time-scale started and the colony in Dolni Vestoniçe was many times older — it was yet learned from both finds that our thoughts would have to be rearranged on the composition of society and culture of prehistoric peoples.

Within the contour of the hut at Unter-Wisternitz (Dolni Vestoniçe) were found artefacts of bone and flint. Yet the most valuable finds were stylized cult figurines resembling the Venus statues illustrated on page 120. Above all, however, it was an ivory figurine of a height of four and a half centimetres which attracted worldwide attention. A wonderfully glistening light issues from this portrait; finely strung, lively, sympathetic and also suffering, a being which stood facing the world devout, pure and humble. This picture, which has all the characteristics of human elevation, even above the richest and most fruitful creations of the Magdalenian, is an inducement to descend once more into the world of the Aurignacian which, without this figure, would seem more distant from us than Utopia.

The destruction of this hunting station and village community is easily reconstructed: a catastrophic dust storm, which probably lasted for days or weeks, poured veritable hillocks of the finest drifting sand over

Fig. 100. The mammoth hunter of Dolni Vestoniçe (Unter Wisternitz) Moravia. Is this the ivory figure of a divine being, a god or goddess? Everything points to the Ice Age hunter having depicted himself.

the place and forced the people to a hurried flight.

Before being confronted by the monumental rock paintings of the Aurignacian, Solutrean and Magdalenian, one can get an inkling from human graves, bear cult sites and small plastics and engravings, of the cultural unfolding of man and the creation of his contemporary interrelations and the composition of his society. To this, pertained the development of the brain and a working speech, in fact, the emergence of the human spirit. Thus were later habits of feeling, of thinking, of a common experience determined. With the emergence of the spirit begins also the inexorable process of self-domestication peculiar to man, he transforms himself, even whilst still a hunter, into a house-holder. "The self-domestication, once it had been finally consolidated" as E. v. Eickstedt explains it "indeed proceeded as if it had long been a matter of course with an obstinate civilizing force. It improved weapons and implements and eventually specialized those manifold forms of scrapers, borers and graters".

In a biological-natural science picture of man the upsurge of the

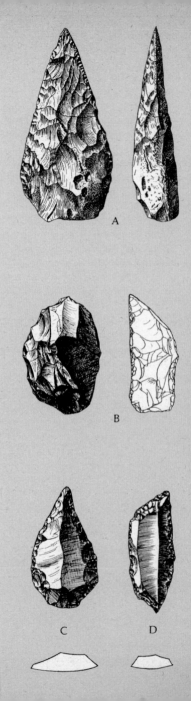

Fig. 101. A) Lancet shaped hand axe of the late Acheulean from St. Acheul (after Commont). It comes from the time of the pre-Neandertal Men and the pre-Sapiens Men and may be 80,000 years old. B) Keeled scraper, C) Scraper point, D) Oblique endscraper on blade (after Riek).

Fig. 102. Leading forms of the Mousterian from La Quina. A) Scraper, B) borer, C) handpoint, D) double point (after Obermaier).

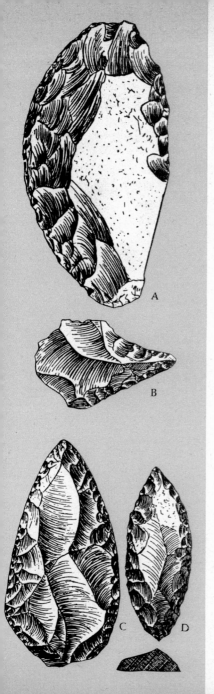

A

B

C   D

human spirit was ascribed nearly always only to the technical skill with which he created his implements. The Ice Age cultures during the course of the last million years were, for instance in Europe, divided into two spheres of culture or race cultures: those with types which had" hand axes" (double faced tools = hand axe industries), core industries; and cultures without hand axes (with flakes knocked off only on one side = Flake industries). The system has been so elaborated, the names of the many industries (for the most part after the names of the French villages where they had been found) are so difficult to remember that it is not easy for an amateur of the subject to master them in a reasonable time without fundamental studies or to impress upon his brain the sequence and shape of the artefacts. A survey on broad lines will have to serve. One remark, however, by Professor W. Gieseler is of importance in connection with the picture of the culture of late Palaeolithic Man: Before the second half of the fourth and last glaciation (and thus about 40,000 years ago) there again emerged out of the lap of the flake culture important industries, they were the blade cultures of the late Palaeolithic, the Aurignacian, Solutrean, and Magdalenian, in the old classical arrangement. Today in the Aurignacian, however, the oldest and the latest cultures are again being named separately (Chatelperronian and Gravettian). For the later presentation of the origin of Homo sapiens it is of great importance that at some places at the end of the last Interglacial or warm period a "pre-Aurignacian" appears and again vanishes, thus particularly in Syria "near the place of discovery, Jabrud". It is not to be forgotten in assessing the value of the stone implements passed on to us that we there are dealing with a purely material cultural possession which would be imperishable. That which had to perish because it was not made of stone was the most important component of all human cultures of the last hundred thousand years. But it was in precisely these perishable materials that lay the treasures which could have given us explanations on the depth of experience, on the imagination, upon the inner spiritual state of innumerable human generations.

Should it be desired to obtain a world-wide appraisal of the human artefacts of the last Ice Age then its disposition would look somewhat as follows:

1. Chopping tools from flaked pebbles of the Australopithecinae.
2. Flakes and cores flaked on both sides (bifaced). Clactonian industry of the second glaciation and Interglacial.
3. Hand-axes and cleavers of the first Interglacial period.
4. Hand-axe cultures and flake cul-

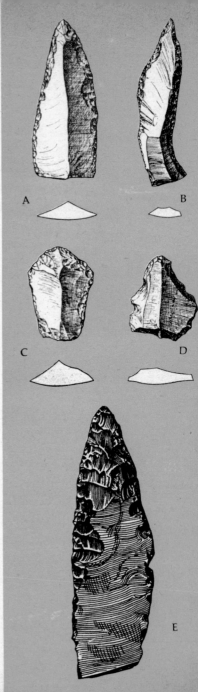

Fig. 103. Finds from the Aurignacian out of the Vogelherd, Stetten ob Lontal (near Ulm). A) blade point, B) coneave side scraper blade, C) blade scraper, D) end scraper (after Rick), E) Artefacts from the Solutrean, willow leaf point from Spy (after Schmidt).

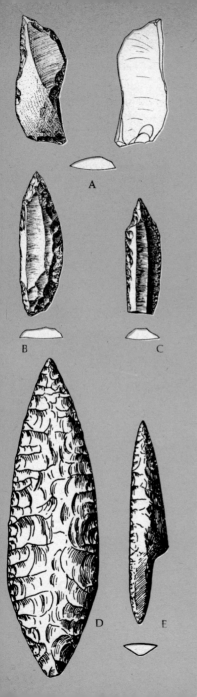

A

B   C

D   E

tures often existed in parallel. People of the warmer climates preferred hand-axes; those of temperate climates flake-tools and one-sided flake artefacts.

The implements which are seen in Fig. 103 and 104 represent the great turning point of late Palaeolithic man. With such pointed blades, notched blades, borers and gravers, Aurignacian man, during the period of the warm fluctuation within the last Ice Age, engraved his pictorial representations and his fanciful faces in stone, ivory or on rock walls. Weapons and implements were constantly being improved. With new lance tips it was no longer necessary to drive rhinoceros and mammoth into ravines and pits: the new leaf-shaped points made it possible to hunt wild horses and reindeer. Weapons and tools were mass-produced wares in industries, they served a barter trade which crossed regional borders and founded a specialized handicraft. "And the knife-blades backed on one edge, side—scrapers, end—scrapers, saw—blades, gravers and planes are the basis of all handicraft up to now" (v. Eickstedt).

Fig. 104. Finds from the Aurignacian at Vogelherd. A) burin, B) trimmed blade point, C) borer on blade (after Rick). Artefacts from the Solutrean. D) laurel leaf point from Laugerie-Basse. E) shouldered point, from Laugerie-Basse (after Schmidt).

IV

MAGIC OF THE PICTURES

The fundamental elements of man's creations were already consolidated quite distinctly in prehistoric times. The probable urges to the making of implements — necessity, want, vision, imagination, or perhaps just pleasure in play with toys — must have been indeed strong. Hitherto, most weight has been placed upon the development of digital dexterity, of "being good with ones hands" with the tools and discoveries, from a primitive beginning to a later completeness. But an idea was mostly awakened at once, dynamic and powerful, filled with spirit and imaginative. The great creations of man reached often to world-wide distances simultaneously. The preparation and completion of a first idea is of secondary importance. Not the slow development, for example, of the flaked hammered pebbles to a throwing spear blade with a hollow base, which has lasted about one million years, decide upon the creative strength of men, but the sudden appearance of an object or tool with vision from natural basic elements. The emergence of the unique idea is the exciting part. In the abyss of time, far from our clear knowledge, man had dreams, his glowing wishes became sudden reality — and before our epoch every-

Fig. 105. Chart of the Ice Age caves and excavation sites, and distribution chart of places of discovery of Ice Age pictorial remains (redrawn after Graziosi).

133

thing was already present in the nucleus.

In our Western realistic, mechanical thinking which wishes to fix a target, the idea prevails that the hand-axe must have been found so as to employ it for some every day purpose alone. In prehistory, however the humdrum did not exist of every day things. Everything, even of our day so much by his tools, nor even through his dead of whom, when all is said, only about 150 individuals with their more or less complete skeletal remains have been unearthed.

The existence of Homo sapiens, of the Palaeolithic, was laid bare first in the 19th century through the extraordinary and unique paintings in

Fig. 106. To the magic of propagation: reindeer subsequently changed into hermaphrodite creatures and a human figure bedecked as a bison blowing a flute. From the cave of Trais Frères (after Begouen and Breuil).

every object completed by man, was a representation of the cosmic and other-earthly world. With the "hand-wedge" as a "stone hand" the might of mankind grew in the magical so that he became human. Homo faber, man the maker, also has his quite unreal side; he remained, even with his useful implement, a Homo magus.

Early Palaeolithic man did not come to the universal consciousness the primeval cult caverns of South-western Europe. The discovery that prehistoric men had had the ability to express in so masterly a manner their environment, their beliefs and the objects of their desires, was incredible and quite beyond grasping. The people of prehistory, so one believed, had existed in a low, half bestial and culture-less primitive condition. And now he was supposed to have created works of art which often even surpassed the creations of Western art. This could not be reconciled with the way of thinking and the historical picture of the last century. The dramatic story of the discovery of Ice Age cave paintings with the destructive criticisms of the international anthropologists and prehistoric archaeologists, who asserted 30,000 or 20,000 years ago had been produced in the dusk or even complete darkness of over one hundred caves of Eastern Spain and Southern France have shattered the overweening self-assurance of the people of our times to their foundations. They have also enlarged illimitably the scope of their historical experience and acquainted them with the

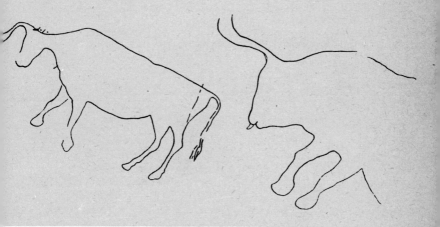

Fig. 107. To the magic of propagation: A bull (incomplete) following a heifer, 62 cm. From the Levanzo cave (Ægades Islands), after Graziosi.

ted the pictures to be conscious forgeries, and finally their recognition at the close of the 19th century belongs to our cultural history and can have no place here. In the confused struggle of beliefs which ended in respectful recognition and with sacrificing scientific diligence, a strong emotion had been aroused which went far beyond the scientifc world. The pictures which 40,000, depth of spirit of their forebears, which can no longer be reached to the same depth and fulness. Their rational, logical line of thought in a technical-mechanical civilization shuts them out of a world so rich. But the roots of our spirit, of our soul, of our world religions, of our philoso-

Fig. 108. Leaping primeval cattle, small horses and net-like figure (perhaps representing a trap). 170 cm. From the cave at Lascaux. ▷

Fig. 109. To the magic of reproduction: pregnant woman and the hind legs of a reindeer, engraved on a fragment of bone, 10 cm. On the reverse side, a picture of a horse, Cave of Laugerie-Basse (Dordogne), after Piette.

phies and thoughtful endeavours and our creative expressions in pictures, and even our social conceptions — they lie in the caves of Altamira, El Castillo, Lascaux, Niaux or Trois Frères. The above are merely some random places in whose subterranean worlds sacred relics of humanity are hidden.

One would like, yet again, to look more closely at the problem of how to imagine these people of tens of thousands of years ago in their physical circumstances, in the state of their soul and their spiritual behaviour.

40,000 years ago the new man, the true Homo sapiens, such as we are,

had spread from Africa to Asia and thence to Europe. And as we distinguish races amongst ourselves, so were the people of the early Palaeolithic also divided from one another by distinct characters. But in them one must not presume so rich a race differentiation as in us. Gigantic areas of land, especially the open park-like landscapes, steppes and savannahs as grazing for the herd animals which could be hunted, were traversed by numerically small tribes, hordes or family groups. The population of the world probably did not even reach the hundred thousand. Again the fossil human finds from this period are so modest that one

Fig. 110. To the magic of reproduction: gravid mare, Cave of Lascaux (Dordogne), after Windels.

cannot dare to arrange them in a genealogical racial order. When, in this connection, one speaks of races of the late Palaeolithic, of a Grimaldi race, a race from Chancelade or of Aurignacians and Cromagnons, then one will name only certain leading types which therefore cannot represent any races in our sense, because the incompleteness of the discoveries is too great. Also, only skeletal remains of them have been preserved not muscles, skin and hair, which distinguish a particular race especially clearly. The bony frame of man also alters very slowly in the course of his genealogical-historical development whilst the race characters of

skin or hair change far more quickly.

In spite of it the savants are not of one mind in their nomenclature. Some researchers put forward a larger number of leading types than others. For the reader who is an amateur it will suffice if two typical late Palaeolithic men are distinguished from one another: the Cromagnons (discoveries at Cromagnon and Oberkassel) and the Grimaldi youth; they were above medium height, 170 cm and over, coarsely built, skull macrocephalic (large headed) but broader than the Aurignacian (discoveries from Combe Capelle, Brünn, Unter-Wisternitz and Chancelade) who was small, long headed and narrow

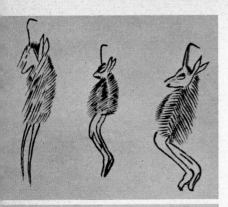

faced. Instead of the brow ridges or roofs over the orbit of the Neandertal man he possessed only powerfully developed eyebrows over each orbit which subsided at the sides. Both human types were representatives of the Caucasoid whose habitat stretched well beyond the Urals, as compared to Europe which we should regard merely as a West-Asiatic peninsula and Eurasia as the geographical habitat of the Caucasoids.

If we confine ourselves to these two leading types then we indeed simplify the discoveries with very differentiated and deviating characters, but one has, as a matter of fact, compromised to be able to say that, to a certain extent, they are the originators of the rock pictures. The question as to whether, perhaps, Cromagnon Man alone was the creator of the carvings remains quite open. To their feeling and their conception of the world we can approach only to a limited degree since, in this, we are standing in our own light. Our rational-logical thought processes make it very difficult to find an approach to them. Yet it can but be attempted.

On page 51 it was indicated how much the large apes, who stand nearest to man, are feeling, picture-

Fig. 111. Representations of dreams, zone of the unreal: on a perforated bone of deer horn are dancing, chamois-pelt covered, human figures. 5 cm high from Abri Mège near Teyat (Dordogne), after Capitan, Breuil, Bourrinet and Peyrony.

Fig. 112. Drawings from the zone of the unreal and dream representations, these pictures come from Altamira cave in Santander Province, Spain (after Benitez).

loving beings which see even objects and living figures plastically before them even if they do not, in fact, exist. Mrs. C. Hayes describes in her book "The ape in our house" how her chimpanzee female Viki played strange and extremely difficult and involved games with a reel of thread which was not present. A subjective *inner* picture ("to imagine something to visualise something") became an quite fairytale-like world in which there are no pragmatic nonparticipants, lifeless things, but only live active beings with which it feels itself to be related. It constructs with their assistance symbols and also magical rites with which it has intimate relationships; it also exchanges identity with them — whether they are pieces of furniture, blankets, pillows, dolls, colours, sounds or ani-

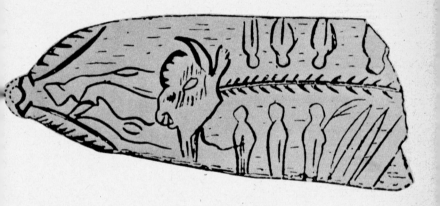

Fig. 113. Representations of the imaginary and dreamlike; on a staghorn bone 8,5 cm long are engraved: men in two ranks, a head, a spine and the fore legs of a bison. Found at Chancelade near Raymonden (Dordogne), after Capitan, Breuil and Peyrony.

outer, plastic tangible awareness — it was an eidetic ability, to be aware (eidos = picture). E. R. Jaensch assumes that human children during their first period of life have perceptions, presentations and eidetic viewing or imaginary, undivided pictures and that in this unity of experience they cannot distinguish between them. Every mother knows that the child grows up in a wonderfully rich, mals. To it all objects in its surroundings are brothers and sisters, even the perceived pictures, which nobody else can see because they actually do not exist. Very soon it comes out of this fairytale, unreal world and the rational experience impoverishes the rich magic in which everything was in heavenly belance.

With this comparison one can perhaps almost transport oneself into the conditions of soul which have preceded us so long a time ago. We cannot now experience the conditions of these people in all things even if we tried to. Our speech, even our words, our understanding, are far removed from this immediate occurrence; we can approach it by memory but never really get near. The prehistoric Caucasoids (or Europeans) never foresook a fairytale existence of enchantment. They remained the "prehistoric super-child". It was the happiest phase of the spirit in the emergence into true man.

As free hunters they did not live in caves — rock overhangs in the open, windscreens, tents and huts were their homesteads — but in the scantily lit underworld, or even in complete darkness, the original European saw open eyed and for him in all reality, whatever he wished to see. It was precisely the twilight or the complete darkness which first made the appearance of the pictures possible; the rock wall seemed to light up and out of the cave-night appeared clearly the imaginary picture whose lines, surfaces and pla-

Fig. 114. Magic rites for the capture and killing of game: a bison, struck by arrows. Below a wild goat partly covered by stalagmites. 51 cm. From the Black Hall in Niaux cave (Ariège).

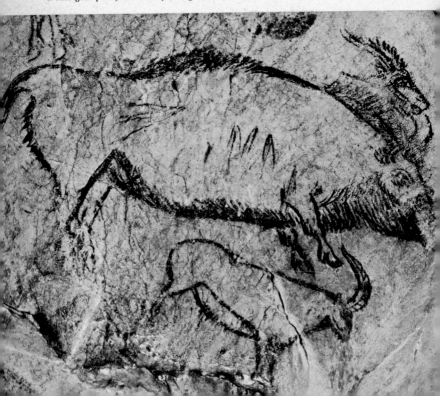

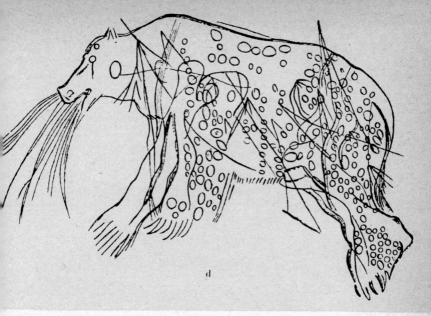

Fig. 115. Magic rites for the capture of and killing of game: bear in the Cave of Trois Frères. It is wounded and bleeding, 60 cm high (after Breuil and Begouen).

stic stereoscopy he had only to scratch in, to follow with a pointed tool and pigment for it to become his own for ever. He saw primeval cattle, bison, wild horse and mountain goat or himself in the mask of an animal, he saw before he had even used graver or crayon, the desired fertility of the animals and how they propagated their kind, he saw the chase and the death of the game as he wished to deal it out by spear or arrow, he saw the trap in which he would catch it and he saw also the spirits he wished to appease and the powerful magical signs with which he would determine the course of his fate — and thus he traced that which appeared before him on the rock wall complete in all detail. Even

outside, round the camp fire, a piece of ivory from the tusk of a mammoth sufficed him, upon which game or human figures appeared of their own accord; one after another they cropped up on the white surface and he engraved them as he saw what "he took for true". Often the first picture vanished and a second appeared beside it equally distinctly. This also would be traced over, then even the first engraving which had resulted from his handiwork and which he could not obliterate at all was no longer visible near the new magic

Fig. 116. The great dark bull above red cattle. Section of the large left hand wall fresco in the Hall of Bulls. Length of the animal: 400 cm. From the cave at Lascaux near Montignac in the departement of Dordogne, Southwest of France. ▷

143

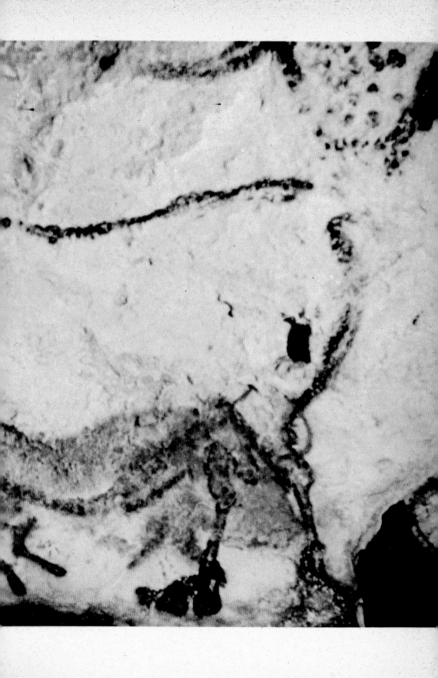

picture. So today one can see a whole series of animal figures raise themselves, for instance, from an engraving of cattle at Limieuil, an engraving of a mammoth from La Madeleine or a horse engraving from Lespugue, from a tangle of lines which seem to twine together, near one another and over one another. The "Vexier pictures" from La Marche which are reproduced here on page 122, in spite of their natural air show the manner of their reproduction exactly; many figures were copied on top of each other at the same time, since before the eyes of the engraver the first pictures of eidetic imagery *and* the actually completed engraving had disappeared. On a new, seemingly empty, surface the picture came up. It may be remarked here that most of the caves which contain rock paintings are limestone caves —

and that lime surroundings promote perceptive ability. Thus, the grotto at Lourdes is also a limestone cavity. In the Espélugues cave, destroyed when building the basilica, were found Palaeolithic cultural relics and late Palaeolithic ivory carvings, magical representations which witness that Lourdes for at least 20,000 years had been a holy place. At this spot then the original European saw his visions

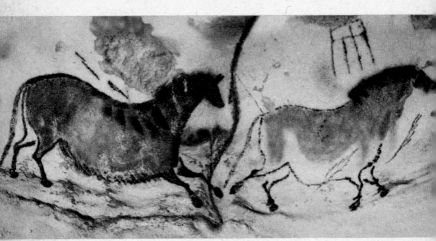

Fig. 117. Magic rites for the capture and killing of game. 140 cm. From Lascaux.

as Bernadette de Soubirous saw hers.

If one looks at the pictures from this point of view; representations to the Magic of propagation, magic rites for the capture and the slaughter of game, pictures of the desired catch of prey as well as pitfalls, the mysterious dream presentations from the regions of the unreal and the wonderful symbols and abstractions *besides* the monumental rock paintings which so amazed us — then the learned word eidetic does not suffice to exhaust the depth of this picture world. It tries to explain that which fundamentally cannot be explained. Assuming the possession of an eidetic talent, only a partly physiological foreground is analysed with our rational material approach. Behind this, however, lies concealed a world feeling for the magical in which everything gets entangled at

pected future. At that time souls had strengthened, thinking had sharpened. High talents separated from the mass, chose the loneliness of the subterranean world and attempted with the help of totems, taboos, oracles and sacrifices to influence the fate of man and the course of life guided by the gods or one God. By incantations and exorcism in the form of their pictures they demanded

Fig. 118: Heads of deer. From Lascaux.

once and all possesses a soul. One must pre-suppose an unbroken, unconscious state of the soul of the original European who was not yet in need of a religion since soul and body were undivided in all that there was and upon which religion can only remind us. Behind the ambient of late Palaeolithic men a thousand invisible forces acted in which a long departed past formed an indissoluble entity with the present and the ex-

a favour of the Divine powers. "It is the flowering time of harmony and feeling of unity with the surrounding world, a time of extraordinary length, of outstanding and fortunate adaptation" (E. v. Eicksted).

In a history of man there is a pertinent question, and one immediately touching us, to be asked. How the rich, blessed world of the original Europeans, which expressed itself in

Fig. 119. Deer. 240 cm. From Lascaux. ▷

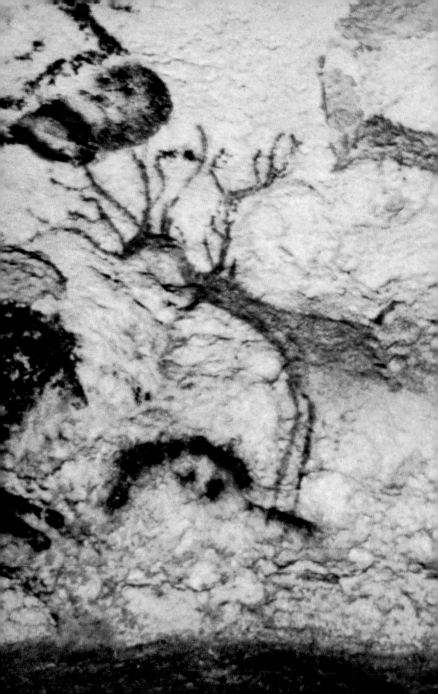

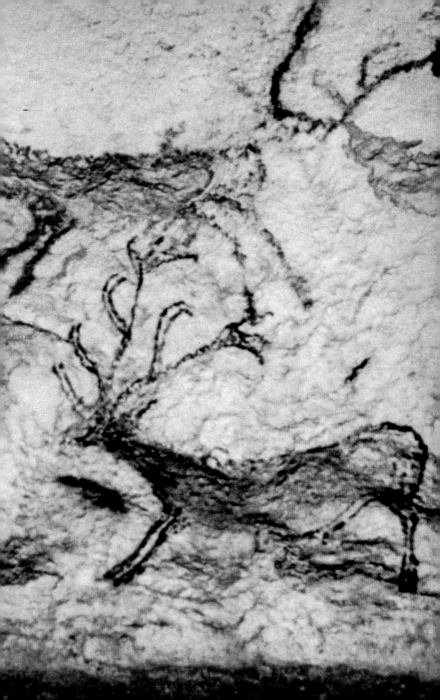

Fig. 120. The "hut" in red and black from the cave of La Mouthe in the Department of the Gironde.

the burgeoning fulness of the pictorial creations, could so suddenly vanish and become impoverished? 10,000 or 12,000 years ago, at least in the Franco-Cantabrian area, the flood of pictures which had been flourishing for 30,000 years was dammed, the powerful streams no longer flowed. Aridity and lack of ornament remained. What had happened?

At the time of the death of the pictures, which almost coincided with the end of the Ice Age, "slash and burn" agriculturalists inhabited the tropical regions of Asia and of the New World. They had replaced the noble, proud and artistic Cromagnons and Aurignacians, the nomadic, free-hunting tribes of the last Ice Age. They avoided the open spaces, the hunting grounds of the hunters, and withdrew into the bush or into the bog lands. There they grubbed up the earth or burnt down the trees to clear their fields, used the digging stick as a spade, stuck or sowed their root plants, taro or yams, in the roughly prepared soil and so founded their matriarchal plant culture. The first planting changed man fundamentally, his soul, his culture, his economy. Man could not discover agriculture, the most radical change in the history of man. He slowly grew towards it, it came, like all cultural change, by itself, often quite in-

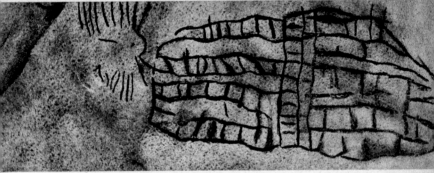

Fig. 121. Symbols, abstractions and various socalled "tectiform" signs from the cave of Altamira.

dependent of man's will it slowly matured. 'The Big Spirit came upon earth', so goes a North American Indian myth, 'and fell asleep. When he awoke he passed through the land. To right and left grew beans and pumpkins, in his footprints ripened the maize and at the place where he slept tobacco took root, the sweet narcotic.' Here representative agricultural plants are named and when one hears that in many tribes the maize god or maize spirit is a woman, a "maize mother", then one also knows that by that time the old patriarchal culture of the hunter has come to an end and that, with agriculture, the matriarchate has again

found a beginning — for the hunters of the Aurignacian of about 40,000 years ago knew no patriarchate, although they lived by the chase.

As breeders of domestic animals the early agriculturalists only succeeded in getting small animals into their power: goat, pig, dog and chicken. The domestic animal as a working animal remained unknown. Even if these tough, unornamented peasants, could no longer make the magnificent, mysterious rock pictures, small plastic figures and carvings of their forebears, and appeared primitive and impoverished, yet they honoured the moon with good reason— motherhood, and fecundity. They had

Fig. 122. Bisons. From Lascaux.

succeeded in an unprecedented creation which was bound to alter the material and spiritual culture of man in a revolutionary manner and which continues to function to this day. The decisive hour for mankind had now struck, had set in motion a destiny which could not be avoided, whether for good or ill. From wild plants man bred useful ones and learnt to improve them by design or accidental choice. With plant breeding and agriculture man encroached upon natural processes; he dominated and guided the natural order of development of living beings. He had emerged from a world which had grown naturally and created for himself, vaingloriously, a world to suit himself alone. With the domestication of plants and animals he domesticated himself.

The primeval slash and burn cultivation encircling the earth with its own well defined culture could have endured to this day without shocks, even without broadening into high civilizations or technified machine cultures had not an event with consequences of the greatest importance occurred: the invention of the plough. Contrary to the development of agriculture and of plant breeding, this was a genuine discovery. An arrangement for attaching a team was made fast to the digging stick

Fig. 123. Cattle. From Lascaux.

or spade and at last the angled branch of the dibber stick was used as a ploughing implement whereupon, by lopping off some of the digging stick, the widened ploughshare was evolved.

It is, however, not only the astonishing technical innovation which altered the world of humanity once more and for ever — it was the second great act of breeding, the breeding of domestic animals which could do work and above all draw the plough. In South East Asia and in India in its widest sense, all five wild cattle have been bred up to domestic use and as draught animals: the ur or aurochs, gaur, banteng, buffalo and yak. No indigenous African cattle have

been domesticated. Only with the arrival of the plough did cereals appear as cultivated forms of corn — barley, wheat, millet or rice nor did domesticated animals do work. The cattle bred created the first means of transport with common wheeled vehicles and the grindstone became a millstone to grind the fruits and seeds in a more rational manner. In the agricultural civilization of the plough child mortality diminished, mankind multiplied rapidly since more people could be fed in a smaller area and the cereals, bread in general, could more easily be stored. By means of draught animals and also by laying down trunk roads, the new plough-plants trade could be exchanged and carried in and out in abundance to peoples at great distances from each other. Droughts and faulty land use brought great hardship on an immensely increasing humanity. At such times of Apocalypse, of homelessness, Homo magus, the magically transcendent man, turned into a Homo faber. The gods and spirits abandoned him, he must trade if he wished to survive. It was, however, the material attainments only, or their loss, which woke a more active, keener spirit, a planning farsightedness, a type capable of higher abstractions. The seeds and bases to a state of philistinism were already sown and laid in the days of spade cultivation. The myths now reminded men only of the innocent paradisiacal conditions of humanity. The wealth of knowledge which piled up and weakened belief would even, at that time, have released old traditions, conventions and strong convictions. Increase in population, intercommunication between groups of folk who had earlier never been in touch; exchange and mixing of cults and gods allowed ancient loyalties to become lost. The spiritual revolutions furthered material successes and the material attainments led the soul of man in ever wider spheres of untrammelled spiritual freedom.

An Amerindian legend admonishes the people: 'Open not the nut lest all things be lost!' But men opened the nut and everything was lost, namely, the things of his magic world. Consciousness awakened. The cold overpowering of nature began and therewith the separation from her. Divinatory powers declined, inspiration, intuition and the approach from within were replaced by a will which spurred on by the imagination and the understanding which had been awake-

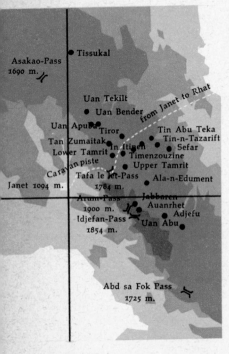

Fig. 124. Map of prehistoric sites at Tassili-n-Ajjer with an inset of the Sahara (after Henri Lhote).

Fig. 125. The Highlands of Tassili-n-Ajjer; a bird's eye view.

Fig. 126. The Great god and worshippers (p. 156/157). The figure in the middle is 3,25 m high. To the left can be seen praying women. Right a probably expectant mother. The fresco has been painted over an older picture which served as background.

ned, appropriated everything with determined tenacity and deliberately created a new material reality. The magic enchantment had been broken and the vision was lost.

Here ends the portion of the history of man which will present his racial history of development: at this point, however, begins his inherited culture and spiritual history passed on in written signs.

Did magical man, with his creative artistic power, come to an end everywhere and at the same time? Did then the discovery of the plough some nine thousand years ago plough up the ancient soul layer of Homo magus?

It continued to live on in North

Fig. 127. Survey of the chief styles of pictorial art at Tassili-n-Ajjer. It has been carried out after Henri Lhote and he himself says of them: "The representations give a survey of the steps to be read from the Tassili paintings. We are, however, dealing with a diagrammatic, incomplete and provisional table. Owing to the abundance of material numerous revisions will be necessary before a complete list, a final balance can be given."
P. 158 from top to bottom: Style of the small horned figures with bullet heads. Style of the imps. Style of the round-headed people of the middle period.
P. 159 from top to bottom: Style of the people with developed bullet heads. Decadent style of the round-headed people. Style of the round-heads under Egyptian influence.

Fig. 128 (p. 160). Two figures of Venus. From the style of the Age of cattle (57 × 57 cm). Small fresco on the wall of a steep declivity. Tamrit.

Fig. 129 (p. 161). The "White Lady" or the "Horned Goddess". In the style of advanced round head type with Egyptian influence (100 × 140 cm). Perhaps, thought Lhote, she is a priestess of the Agrarian cult, for the horns seem to carry a field of corn from which the grains fall. The colours used are yellow and white.

Africa in the Sahara. The existence of prehistoric rock-pictures in the South Atlas and mid-Sahara was known from the year 1847 when French officers in a campaign against rebellious tribes found the first rock drawings. Heinrich Barth, the great German African traveller, discovered during his expeditions in the Libyan desert between the years 1848 and 1855, some prehistoric pictures which were later copied and published by Frobenius and Graziosi. It was known also from carvings and rock paintings in the North Eastern part of the Hoggar massif. The sites of the discoveries lay in the highlands of Tassili, a gloomy and often almost inaccessible country. This dead and silent mountain range with columns, precipices, eroded rock bastions, with thousands of cavities and ravines, seems to have been lifeless even in primeval days. The Tassili-n-Ajjer, to be accurate, which lies west of Egypt and south of Benghazi, presents a terrible view from the air: the mazes of jumbled rocks are weathered so regularly that they resemble gigantic but deserted blocks of houses with a network of exactly divided streets which no longer belong to any earthly region. It is a nightmare picture of mountains or the show-place of a strange constellation in which nothing exists which can be compared in the remotest degree to anything on earth.

A Lieutenant Brenans, officer-in-charge of a troop of camel men (meharistes) had discovered in this desert, before the second war, wall

carvings and rock paintings which, after the war, led Dr. Henri Lhote to a quite unprecedented work of exploration in 1956 and 1957. He and his collaborators gained a vast purview over ten thousand rock-pictures which greatly exceeded in numbers the rock paintings of Europe. Thus, at Tassili was found the largest museum of prehistoric art in the Western hemisphere. Eight thousand years before our time this hell of stark rock cones, rock cliffs, ravines and bastions was immensely lively. Until the last years before Christ the original inhabitants of the Sahara lived in the cavities, recesses and rock chambers. For 8,000 years man secured his exorcisms, prayers and cult celebrations in pictures on his rocky walls.

Often in places twelve thicknesses of pictures were superimposed upon one another, which for millennia serv-

Fig. 130. Continuation of Lhote's survey of the principal styles in pictures at Tassilli-n-Ajjer.
P. 162 from top to bottom: Style of the hunters with painted bodies of the Old cattle age period. Cattle age style. Style of the "Judges" of the period after the Cattle age.
P. 163 from top to bottom: Style of the white tall people of the period after the Cattle age. Style of the Cart period. Style of the Double Triangle men, period of the Riding horse.
Out of the more than ten thousand rock paintings discovered by Lhote four great periods detach themselves with approximately twelve style elements: one epoch of the hunter, which existed for three thousand years from 8000 to 5000 B.C., a second epoch of herdsmen with tamed cattle, from 5000 to 1200 B.C. and a third epoch of the warriors with carts and war chariots from the time of the second People's storm before 1200 B.C. In the fourth and last group which appears in the years about 50 B.C. the camel, imported from Asia to Africa, is decisive.

ed religious worship. The grandiose frescos show in colours which are today still fresh and undisturbed: gods and godesses, demons and spirits, hunters, dancers, swimming and running people with their hunting animals, giraffes, ostriches, antelopes, mouflons, hippopotamuses and elephants. Light reed boats, men swimming and the species of animals bear witness, to the fact that the stony wilderness must at one time have been fertile land. The central Sahara was then a well populated and densely settled region with well-watered and fertile valleys and meadows. Even now, the ancient beds of streams, rivers and brooks can be recognised which at one time watered the present desert region in a gigantic network.

Henri Lhote was also able to indicate that primitive military roads had crossed this region in prehistoric ages. The North-South Africa route had been a busy popular road. Caucasoids or Europeans from the last Ice Age, light skinned Orientals and Southern Europeans pushed forward as far as the Transvaal. The "White Lady of Tsissab", a rock painting on the South African Brandberg, has, among other fresco figures, North African, Egyptian and Cretan characteristics. From all this it appears that even in Neolithic in Post-Glacial times Neolithic magic man with his abundance of pictures, his primordial cults and his faith in nature, still lived upon earth. What Lhote had seen in his 80,000 kilometre journey as rock painting and rock carving were the documents of manifold cultures which could spread in a blessed land in an unbroken sequence of 8,000 years. As the "People of the war-chariots" arose, of whom the pictures also inform us, the height of the Saharan fertility was past. The rivers gradually ceased to flow. The horse vanished and shortly before the Ancient Greeks and Romans, the camel was introduced from Asia, the animal bred of the desert.

Long before this final alteration of the ancient Saharan pastures and Sahara savannahs into lifeless wastes and before the destruction of the mountain forests where nowadays only parched, barren chasms gape, even before the millennia of lush fertility, similar periods of aridity may have annihilated equally fruitful country. Perhaps men were forced many times to quit this land for the south.

The remains of human skulls and limb bones which were found at Boskop in the Transvaal belong to a primitive human race who probably immigrated from the North. They may even have beaten a trail before the last Ice Age — a repeatedly trodden popular road stretching from North Africa to the Cape, the length of the African Continent.

Only after the Finnish savant, Tallgren, had reported comprehensively in 1932 upon rock pictures of North and Central Asia did the West become aware in the broadest sense of the results of archaeological research of the Academy of Science of the U. S. S. R. The Asian rock pictures in their widely dispersed abundance put the Franco - Cantabrian and North African prehistoric pictorial creations completely in the shade. They were discovered, in part even two hundred years ago, from the Urals to the river Amur and from the Pamirs to the river Lena. They are especially well distributed in the gigantic curve of the mountains of the Pamirs, Tienshan, Altai, and Sajan and even in the steppe region eastward of Lake Baikal. In Shishkino alone, on the upper Lena in a stretch of one and a half kilometres of a bare sandstone outcrop, 2,700 paintings were found and at Sajmaly Tash on the ridge of Ferghana over 100,000 rock pictures! In addition, there are eleven important Central Asian and Siberian rock picture sites, which had always been cult sites. In terms of time these quantitatively largest relics of humanity reach to an epoch corresponding to the European Magdalenian, some 15,000 years ago. Without material interruption they lead from before the Neolithic right through to the last few centuries of our time. In animal and human portraits, hunting scenes and boat processions, sun worship cults, journeys of the dead to the Underworld, clannish sacred relics and deerlike animals (Cervidae) all are venerated as cosmic symbols. R. Grahmann remarked in 1952 in his book "Urgeschichte der Menschheit" ("Original History of Humanity"): "From Siberia ancient cultures are not known and on climatic grounds hardly to be expected."

V

THE LAST OF ANCIENT MAN
AND THE BEGINNING OF RACES

That we can reanimate the distant
extinct world of the Aurignacians only
in the documents of their creative
picture-art must be said with reservations. There still exist today near us,
indeed mingling with us, the "shores
without history" which Alexander von
Humboldt investigated among the natives of the Orinoco. There are still
people of eternal primordial time who
live like ancient men or survivals in
a restricted, timeless world. If we do
not waste a single day more or allow
a year to pass and set out on journeys
with a self-imposed task and the vol-
untary dedication of researchers like
Martin Gusinde or Paul Schebasta —
then we may dip once again into this
primeval world of man. Yet to do this
means to give up completely our civilized customs and traditions and our
habits of thought, and an acceptance
of vexations and hardships which are
often intolerable.

We should have to visit the Australoids, the Aboriginal inhabitants of
Australia, and to live with them, and

Fig. 131. The development of the races in the
Upper Paleolithic is as yet unknown. For
Europe only variants in a very rough survey
can be named: the Aurignacians which are
represented by the finds at Combe Capelle,
Brno, Predmost or Chancelade — and the Cromagnons represented by the finds at Cromagnon and Obercassel. From the top: human
skulls from Predmost in Moravia, the "Old
Man of Cromagnon". Skull from Obercassel.
Skull from Chancelade (after v. Eickstedt).

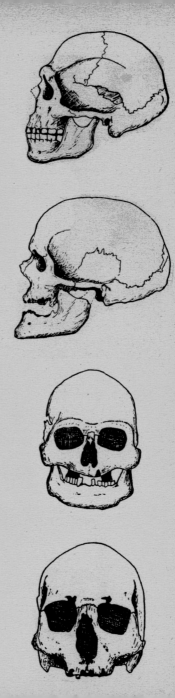

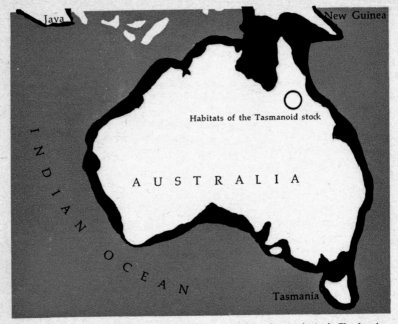

Fig. 132. This is the manner in which Tasmania could have been colonised. The Ice Age, with its ice caps and glaciers, froze so much water that the sea surface lay lower than today. The present covered regions which were earlier dry are drawn black (redrawn after Tindale and Lindsay).

the Bambuti pygmies in the African primeval forest, the Bushmen of the Kalahari desert, the Semang in the Malay Peninsula or the equally dwarf- ish tribes in the Andamans, the Philippines or New Hebrides Islands.

The list may be lengthened with the namens and places of the Veddahs of Ceylon, India and Burma, the Ainus of the northern Japanese Islands and the mountain Papuans in New Guinea. But as the original prim-

Fig. 133. The last surviving Tasmanian. Drawing of a photograph of about 1875. The Tasmanians at one time wandered all over Australia where they colonised Tasmania where they were eventually extirpated by the whites. It was a mystery how they crossed the wide Strait — the Bass Strait — between Tasmania and Australia for they had no seaworthy craft. The Tasmanians do not belong to the Australoids, probably they are a primeval branch of the Caucasoids or Negroids.

ordial, genuine descendants of the European Aurignacians, only the Australoids can really be counted!

The Australoids had hitherto lived in their deserts and in the bush-lands of North-Western Australia, protected by the intervening great continental distance, almost like the Sapiens people of the early times when they had overcome the Neandertalers and left them behind. Hitherto — for now even such conservative tribes as the Njangomada, the Garadjara and Mangala have been drawn in by the suction of the highly civilized world-machine culture. When the Australian Aborigines know how to use bank-notes, motor vehicles, radiogramophones, carpet sweepers, sewing machines and cameras then there has

Fig. 134. Two dancing mythical figures. Drawing by the Aborigines of Australia representing the "Two Creative Beings".

Fig. 135. Natives of North-west Australia, "Australoids". Beside the three main races, Caucasoids, Mongoloids and Negroids they occupied a special position.

Fig. 136. A family of jungle Papuans in the South-East of New Guinea. They represent the dark-skinned equatorial races who, during the Ice Age, immigrated from South-East Asia. Even the piglet to be seen in the picture is part of the family. It is tenderly treated and suckled after the children by the wife.

occurred here more than the destruction of a tribal stock or local groups within the tribes, there is vanishing the last evidence of a spirit and an attitude of the soul which has endured for 40,000 years. Certainly the immense wealth of experiences of the original Sapiens men was impoverished and became blunted inside them, but out of their cultish-religious ceremonies, out of the remnants of their imaginary beliefs and surrenders one can still get some idea of the mighty richness of the Aurignacian. In spite of this, what is happening now before our eyes is something stupifying and peculiar: the doubtful material good

of the whites is accepted only outwardly, with inner reservations and is not valued highly; nor yet has it got power over their souls. The tough conservatism exercised through millennia has not yet been broken. The white is for him merely a "wailbili", a white, a man without laws. They leave him when the calendar of their community-life, the primordial law, calls them to the sacred places of their tribe in the bush. Each member of the clan returns at the correct time of the year, which is known only to the clan or horde itself, to his clan or horde, which is a subordinate of the tribe whose hunting grounds they share in common. They also, however, take part in the inter-tribal cultural feasts in which several tribes unite. Corroborees (as these tribal gatherings are called) are carried out in secret places from time to time. By primeval legendary, or historical tradition they follow the ritual obligations which alone guarantee their existence and without which they could not live. Our speech and forms of expression cannot reproduce this mythical-religious reality. The Australoids live timelessly in the truest sense of the word: they do not know any time. In their dim past it was the "Two men and creator beings" who brought everything to life, who preserve life in everything and who will also pre-

Fig. 137. Bushman and wife.

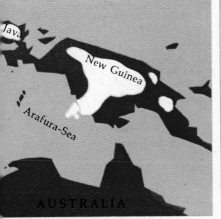

Fig. 138. Survey map of New Guinea showing its unexplored or poorly explored regions (redrawn after Schmitz).

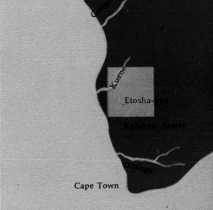

Fig. 139. Map of South West Africa. The grey quadrangle shows the habitat of the Bushmen. They were the first colonists of the whole South African region. After gruesome persecution they retreated to the Kalahari desert and to Ojinpolo in Portuguese Angola.

169

Fig. 140. Veddahs. The Veddahs of Ceylon, India and Malaya belong to a primeval race near to the Europoids.

serve everything in the future – if they are always remembered. In the ceremonial dramatic-mimic dances, in the earnest gripping hymns which had been sung with equal fervour thousands of years ago, the two creators awake in each year to new life and to new activity. They combine past, present and future – as we should express it. But for these Believers there is no past; the future also has been foreclosed. The original beginning is taking place now and at this moment. The Australoids do not know any historically developing outer or inner life; they cannot conceive a beginning or an end to their life. Every-

thing is always in the present; the past is interwoven with the present and the future — but only if the laws are respected, the laws of belief, of the ceremony and the cult of the united tribal stock. With the breaking of the laws the world of the Two men would at once break up and thus the end of the world would come.

From our point of view — and the Australoid can follow our train of thought just as little as Aurignacian man could have — fervid, imaginary, dedicated, timeless belief is justified and has become the "truth" because it has been preserved through the storms of an immense length of time. These Ancient men the oldest on earth, have really an "eternal", unbroken, continuous life behind them.

With them the foundation layer of the Aurignacians is always shining — until now it has for them been imperishable.

The pygmy in the African primeval forests does not represent any "original" form of mankind like the Australoids. He descends from much-ramified collateral branches and was finally decimated by stronger more progressive human groups, driven to refuge districts and became impoverished in a frightful, unfriendly environment, to which he was able to adapt himself only by extreme specialization. Even if he is not an immediate descendant of an ancient line yet he descends from archaic human branches and their inherited characteristics survive in him so primevally primitive that a hellish habitat had to become his protection; none wishes to take it from him.

Materially, the pygmies are still below the Stone Age men. They do not know any stone implements; their tools and weapons are fashioned from bamboo and wood. Thus the Australopithecines one million years ago with their stone tool technique were far in advance of them. The pygmies are for us today an exact image of primeval man even if no continuity of stock exists between the original men and the pygmies.

The dwarfish forest man of tropical Africa is a restless game catcher without any agriculture at all. The women and girls collect small beasts and gather fruits, seeds, tubers and roots; the men hunt antelopes and monkeys. For a European the true tropical primeval forest is an intolerable inferno with its gloom, its hot house atmosphere and its noxious steamy vapours. Only at great heights does the heavy roof thin out, composed as it is of treetops, leaf mould, tangles of branches, matted twigs with swollen plant tumours, of epiphytes, parasites, lianas and mosses. The impenetrable cover allows no ray of sunlight to penetrate. Below on the ground between the bare trunks and the lianas, growing vertically in strands as thick as a thigh, dusk reigns, or even thick darkness. The ground is covered by heavy layers of rotting plants which emit a sickly sweet smell of decay. The hanging, constantly dripping lianas, are to the Bambuti pygmies in every sense veritable Jacob's ladders which carry them to a network of paths high above the ground. Up there lies the other dimension of their world which they have had possession of for thousands of years, shaped of a network of twigs, branches and lianas which they traverse as surely as the forest paths down below. The Bambuti in the Ituri Forest knows his supra-terrestial "road network" which carries him securely through the heights above the twilight of the wilderness. The paths, even when laid high above in the foliage of the trees, are tribal property and are tribal heirlooms. They are

Fig. 141. The maximum glaciation in Eurasia (about 100,000 B. C.). Ice cover and frozen-ground white and gray; dark blue = old sea surfaces or saltings. — In this Ice Age development-area there arose with great probability the three great races, Europoids (Caucasoids), as Western humanity, Mongoloids as Eastern humanity and Negroids as Southern humanity.   ▷

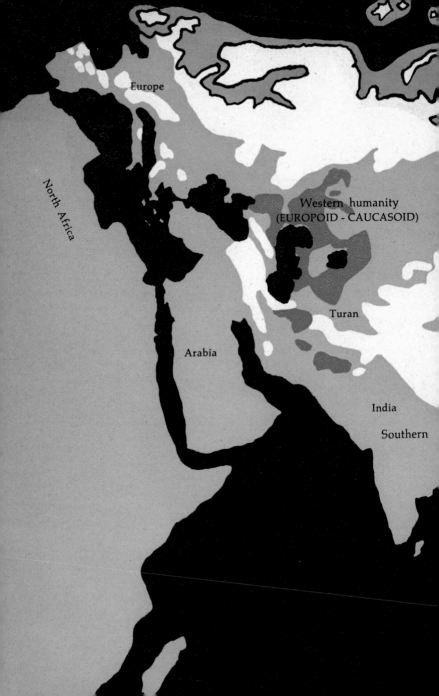

Siberia

Eastern humanity
(MONGOLIDS)

Tibet

China

humanity
(NEGROID)

Indo China

holy, which means full of magic power-er, for they are saturated with the life of the tribe and hence are really living beings. Everything manifest here on earth, particularly tribal action and tribal property, is also the action and possession of the supernatural powers.

The Bambuti still possess the natural faith and vision of their ancestors. It is the belief in the complete unity of nature in which everything is fundamentally the same, where each object can change its shape and transform itself into the incomprehensible since everything represents only the cloak of a single mystical power — therefore nothing need be investigated for its quality. In this one and individual world in which heaven and earth, man and heaven and man and earth are not yet separated, where there is as yet no division between some one on this side and one on the other all human conditions and possessions and their forebears are contained in the depth of time.

Only from this unbroken magical state of the soul can the Bambuti be understood correctly, and also their forefathers in the depth of time, whom we only know as fossils or through their pictures.

With his spoors and his paths, with game and fruit gathering, with the multiplicity of his signs and the characteristics of this world, in which he sees all, hears all, and scents all and in which no leaf movement, no smell, not the softest sound escapes him, the Ituri world lays itself bare to him by these means. And behind the Ituri surroundings there acts continuously, with a thousandfold strength, the invisible magic Ituri in which the distant past forms an indissoluble entity with the present and the future.

When neighbouring negroes squatted in the forest the light-coloured pygmies, who are not negroid, said: "This forest belongs to us; we allow the negroes to live here near us." The Bambuti pygmies recognise no authority, no orders, nor an organisation under a chieftain. The female has equal rights. "The pygmies are impatient, impulsive and capricious. They have indescribable vitality, they are the most dance-loving people on earth." (P. Schebasta)

"In a pygmy community things are always cheerful and peaceful. As bearers of an ancient human cultural form the pygmies were, and are, not addicted to uninterrupted fighting or prolonged quarrelling. From a lively sense of duty everyone stayed, and remains, in his own nomadic territory and his own clan; thus encounters over the common property of the others and more especially over the very modest private property, are avoided. All human life enjoys the highest value, there neither was, nor is there now, any abortion, murder or the abandonment of the sick or weakly old. Equally unknown among the primeval hunters — whether they are pygmies or not — is almost any form of cannibalism." (M. Gusinde)

So shines even to this day, in Australoid and pygmy, a last glow of ancient human culture, whose light would dazzle us intolerably for in it we would have to lose our self esteem. If one cannot idealize anything — for the life of these primitive men is incredibly hard — yet from them we can obtain a true picture of a history of people, if one remembers that on the absence or loss of material riches, that is with a primitive diet, high culture is not excluded. And the principal criterion of a culture is humanity. Thus, in this way also one arrives, by means of cultural psychology and behaviour-research, close to the history of man.

The gold-brown Bushmen in Western South Africa show just as little of the negro as do the Bambuti. According to racial characteristics, the Bushmen are included with the Hottentots in the Khoisan group (Hottentots = Khoi-Khoin, i.e. Men, and San = Bush-folk) for they resemble each other outwardly by their fat rumps (steatopygy), the "Hottentot apron" (a prolongation of the labiae minorae) the high thoracic situation of the breasts and by the typical peppercorn hair (fil-fil) which allows the skin of the scalp to show in between the tuft's. The taller Hottentots have become nomadic herdsmen, whilst some of the Bushmen have remained hunters like the Bambuti, although in other respects they have nothing in common. It is astonishing that the fat-bottom formation and the typical in-curvature of the vertebral column, which is quite unique and has occured nowhere else except in the Andaman islanders, was found in a statuette discovered on the Riviera of late Palaeolithic origin. Although the Mongoloid

cover fold of the eyelid in Bushmen is striking, the investigators on heredity say this is no sign that they belong to the great Mongoloid race. This characteristic is in Europeans a "concealed" recessive inherited characteristic whereas in the Mongoloids it is dominant. At all events, the Khoisan people, and, in a special sense, the Bushmen, take up just such a separate position within the three great races of Caucasoids, Mongoloids and Negroids as the Australoids, whom also one cannot place within the white, yellow or black races. Not only the above-mentioned characteristics but also the unique kind of cutaneous ridges of the papillar bodies and the unusual formula for their blood groups allow the Bushmen to appear as an independent race. And since the Hottentots correspond with the Bushmen in those characteristics, it is believed that the Khoisan peoples are descended from the ancient African series of primitive Caucasoids. In this primeval human type, with his materially lowest total economy, there may still be distinguished with the greatest clarity the true features of the Sapiens race of the earliest times.

Once upon a time — the time of their immigration is not known — they were the first Colonists of South Africa. The Bushmen — and it is of them only that we speak here — were forced to take flight by the so similar Hottentots, driven northward by the Euro-

Fig. 142. Survey of the most important race systems by v. Eickstedt, Deniker, Coon, Czekanowski, Biasutti and Hooton (after Schwidetzky). ▷

175

EUROPOIDS

v. EICKSTEDT	DENIKER	MONTANDON
Nordide	Nordique	Blonde
East europids	Orientale or Vistulienne	
Alpine (including Lappids)	Occidentale	Alpine and Lapponienne
Dinarides	Adriatique	Adriatique
Armenides	Assyroids	Anatolienne and Pamirienne
Turanids	Turco-tartare	Touranienne
Orientalides	Arabe	Arabe
	Ibero-Insulaire	Ibero-Insulaire
Mediterraneans	Literale	
	Berbere	Berbere
Indids	Indo Afghan	Indo Afghan

NEGROIDS

v. EICKSTEDT	DENIKER
Sudanide	Negre
Nilotide	(Negritienne)
Kafferide	Negre (Bantou)
Palenegride	
Ätheopide	Ethiopienne
Indomelanide	Dravidienne
Neomelaneside	
Palemelaneside	Melanesienne
Bambutide	Négrito (Negrille)
Negritide	Négrito (Negrits)
(Australide	Australienne
Khoisanide)	Bochimane

MONGOLOIDS

v. EICKSTEDT	DENIKER
Tungide	Nord mongolide
Sinide	Sud mongolide
Palemongolide	
Sibiride	Ugrienne
Eskimide	Eskimienne

EUROPOIDS

COON	CZEKANOWSKI	BIASUTTI
Nordic and Brünn race	Nordic	Nordide
Ladoga race	Subnordic	Baltide
Alpine	Alpine	Alpide
Lapps	Lapponoide	Lappide
Dinaric and Norish	Dinaric	Adriatide
Armenoids	Armenoids	Armenide
		Turanide
		Orientalide
	Mediterranean North western	Mediterranide
Mediterranean		
		Berberide
Irano-afghanian		Indide

NEGROIDS

MONTANDON	HOOTON
Soudanienne	African Negro
Nilocharienne	Nilotic Negro
Sud Africaine	African Negro
Paleotropicale	
Dravienne	
Papouasienne	Melanesian-Papuan
Pygmeenne	Negrito
Australienne	Australians
Steatopygienne	Bushman-Hottentot
Tasmanienne	Tasmanians

MONGOLOIDS

MONTANDON	HOOTON
Toungousienne Nordmongolienne	Classic mongoloid
Sinienne Paréene Paléosibirienne	Indonesian-Mongoloid
Esquimienne	Arctic-mongoloid (Eskimoid)

pean immigrants of the 17th century, chased by the warlike Kaffirs and decimated and eventually, in modern days, reduced to 10,000 survivors by the white settlers of the Boer farms', in regular driven battues. Apart from the numerous families which joined the farms as labourers, the remaining Bushmen peoples live as free desert hunters at the centre of the Kalahari and in the sandy waste of the Ojinapolo in the South East of Portuguese Angola. As trappers of game and hunters they produce just as little as the Bambuti in their forests but how very different is their world from that of the pygmies. In the merciless, sun-scorched desert and dry steppe it rains only during eight consecutive weeks. If everyone cannot fill 30 ostrich egg shells with water as a store in this scanty rainy season then his life is in considerable danger. They close the opening in the egg shell with grass and bury their treasure in the sand. Of course, they understand also how to suck water up from below the sand with hollow stalks, from troughs or old hollow fig trees — yet often even these sources are quite dried up. They carry a strip of leather as a hunger belt which they lace firmly round their belly when hunger plagues them. Hunting is carried out with bows and poisoned arrows and the women know the time of year at which they are able to harvest tubers, roots, fruits, pods and nuts, besides which they catch snakes and lizards.

Thus they live not very differently to the way Australopithecines may have lived in a like or similar environ-ment, in the same clannish community, in the same isolated spaces. It is not unlikely that this simple economy must have led to similar, if not the same, behaviour. The spiritual attitude and the souls of these later heirs will approximate to those of their original forebears. If information is obtained on the form of economy, social structure and psychic behaviour of these ultimate members of an immensely long and uniform series of generations then it is really not too bold to draw some conclusions from them on the general existence of their primeval forefathers, even with the reservation that impoverishment, and decadence has weakened the present men. From these degenerate remnants, the relics of a formerly overwhelming flood of life one can still well imagine the vital unbroken strength of their genus.

The account of an Englishman, Selwyn James, who describes an accidental and not even highly dramatic encounter with a Bushman in the Kalahari desert, is worth a whole series of dry and painstaking works of investigation and plumbs the depth of a beautifully limpid, simple soul. James shortened his motor journey to Windhoek by 1800 kilometres because he chose the lonely, dangerous route through the Kalahari. Midway across the desert the radiator of his car ran out of water and in the murderous heat he sat there far from all human settlement. After some hours a Bush-

Fig. 143. Expanded race systematics after Eickstedt. List of minor names for individual races.

EUROPOID

EUROPE
Nordid
Dalofalic
East-europid
Mediterranid
Alpine
Dinarid

AFRICA
Berberid/Eurafricanid
Mediterranid
Orientalid
Nilotid K

Ancient Stratum
Bambutid P
Khosaide (P)

ASIA
(East) Mediterranid
Orientalid
Armenid
Turanid
Gracilindid
Indobrachid

Ancient Stratum
Veddid
Gondid/Malid
Ainuid
Andamanid P
Semangid

INDONESIA/OCEANIA
Polynesid K

Ancient stratum
Palemelanid
Neomelanid
Australid
Aetid P
Mountain-papua (P)

MONGOLOID

ASIA
Tungid
North-Sinid
Mid-Sinid
South-Sinid

Palemongolid
Palaungid
Shanid

INDONESIA/OCEANIA
Protomalayid
Deuteromalayid

AMERICA
Eskimid

North Indianid
Pacifid
Centralid
Silvid
Margid

South Indianid
Andid
Patagonid
Brasilid
Lagid
Fuegid

NEGROID

AFRICA
Sudanid
Nilotid K
Kafrid
Palenegroid

K = Contact race between two great races
P = Pygmies

Fig. 144. Survey map of the division of the great races in 4000 B.C. (which see). The anthropologist G. Kurth drew the maps shown here and on pp 184/185 and 188/189. In this simplified and diagrammatic presentation he attempted to reproduce three cross sections through the distribution of the great races on earth from 4000 B.C. to 1500 A.D. The dark coloured areas show rallying points.

man armed with bow and arrow approached him. James did not dare to leave his car since the tales of their duplicity, cruelty and cunning had made him mistrustful. The native remained standing motionless for an hour in front of the car and stared at James; then put his bow and arrow on the ground, raised his hands as a sign of peace, laughed and spoke his clicking tongue and seemed finally quite unable to understand and was concerned that James did not get out.

The Bushman remained near the car all day and in the evening he lit a fire from dry brushwood and enomia twigs, for it became cold. When James woke next morning the small Bushman was squatting cross legged on the bonnet of the car. At his loin-cloth hung a bladder chockfull of water. Now, at last, James ventured to leave his car and was able to make clear to him by gestures that he wanted water for his radiator. "He took them as gestures of trust and hopped about as happy as a sandboy". With a hollow stem he sucked out water from the sandy ground in the vicinity of the camp where an underground spring existed. The bladder was refilled several times before the water gave out. When James wished to give

the Bushman his gold wrist watch as a present he felt it delicately with trembling fingers and then handed it back. And when James pressed him to take it he would not allow it, he pleaded with his eyes not to drive him to it not to force him into such shameful behaviour, "You are, after all, my guest" his eyes seemed to say. "This is my desert, my home. I do not want any payment for my hospitality."

In a canvas bag James drew off some water from the radiator for his friend and demanded in a determined tone that he should take it. The Bushman's eyes grew moist and his lips trembled. "We then parted company, both of us — this I am certain — convinced of the warm feelings of the other. During our short comradeship

our hearts had bridged the ages which separated our two worlds. Here was a man who was filled with true unselfish love for his fellow-men." That evening James discovered the water-filled canvas bag on the floor of the car. "My little Bushman, God bless him, had replaced it there."

Complete humanity and complete inner penetration of nature — these are the elementary foundations of a culture. All else which is built upon these elements with spirit and purpose is derived from it.

As a final picture of the last primeval men, and one from which we recognise the texture of the soul of Sapiens man of 40,000 years ago, we have an Eskimo. It is Knud Rasmussen, whose mother, incidentally, was an Eskimo, who reported on the chieftain of the Padlermiut tribe, Igjugarjuk. One day he said to Rasmussen: "All true wisdom one finds only far from man, out in the great loneliness, and it may be attained only through suffering. Abstinence and suffering are the only things which can open the mind of man for that which is hidden from others."

And Rasmussen went on to tell more about him: "As a young man Igjugar-

Fig. 145. European racial types:
A Swede   B Woman from Central Germany   C Swiss

juk had many dreams which he could not explain. Wonderful beings whom he did not know approached him and spoke to him and when he awoke from sleep all his dream pictures were there so much alive that he could repeat all about them to his camp mates. After it had become clear in that way that he was intended to become a magician an old man called Perqanaoq became his tutor. In the middle of winter at the coldest time, he took Igjugarjuk on a small sledge, just big enough to sit upon, far from the camp to the other side of the Hikoligjuak. Here he had to remain sitting on the sledge whilst the old magician built him an ice hut which was so small that he could only just crouch inside it. Igjugarjuk was not allowed to sully the snow with his footsteps and was therefore carried into the snow hut by the old man. He received no more than a small piece of pelt to sit on, he also got no food whether dry or wet. The old magician reminded him to think only of the Great Spirit and of the leading spirit who would now come to him. He then departed and left him. When five days had gone by the old magician came back and brought him a sip of tepid water. Thereupon he fasted again, and to wit for fifteen days, and again received another mouthful of lukewarm water with a quite small piece of meat and then had to fast for another ten days. After this long fast he was at last brought back by the magician. Igjugarjuk told that the thirty days

Fig. 146. Afrikan racial types:
A Woman from Ethiopia   B Hottentot   C Bushman

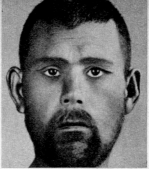

D Man from East Germany   E Russian   F Greek

that he spent at that time were so cold and exhausting that at times he died a little. He thought during the whole time only of the Great Spirit and tried to keep all thoughts of people and all daily events out of his mind. Only towards the end of his fast there came a guiding spirit in the form of a woman whilst he slept, and hovered over him. Then he no longer dreamt of her and she became his familiar spirit.

After the cold and the hunger of this long month he had to keep a very severe diet for another five months and have no intercourse with women. Then the fast was repeated, for the oftener it is repeated the more capable one is of seeing that which is concealed from others. In fact, initia-

tion is never finished; it depends on oneself how much one wants to endure and how much learn. Behind the account of the initiation of this future shaman one seems to see the powerful eyes of the magician from the cave at Trois Frères. And the skeleton of the man from Chancelade in the Dordogne, an Aurignacian, would be regarded as an original Eskimo. Even if that is doubtful we do know that there survives in the Eskimo generally, early Palaeolithic characteristics.

Only now does the question come to the fore how, after the actual origination of men has such a differentation come to pass amongst mankind? How could they develop into Caucasoids, Mongoloids, Negroids and Australoids, Pigmies or Bushmen? Wha

D South African   E Woman from the Eastern Congo   F West African

Fig. 147. Survey map of the great race distribution about the time of Christ.

forces were at work which separated human kind, which one can imagine as unified at first, and of equal stature, into so many races and distributed over the entire globe? What became of the "human hominids" when the "animal-to-man" field of transition had been overcome? Did the splitting up of humanity into races perhaps already lie in the womb of time before the becoming of man? The anatomist and anthropologist, Klaatch, supported the idea that the three great races, white, yellow and black had three animal primaries as forebears: the Caucasoid to descend from the Chimpanzee, the Mongoloid from the orang-utan and the Negroid from the gorilla. But the characters of man are in their basic features, and also in their various details, so much in agreement that one must say: present humanity comes from one root. The picture of a root, however, does not say at the same time that man developed from one stem. The splitting up of roots in man lies in the immense abysses of time in which the apes of the Old World also developed parallel to the line of man, in their own genealogical way. The coming of man thus did not ensue several times, but the various human types and human races were created at different times and at different places.

You are now invited to remember the remarks on the original native land of man on page 95 in the second

Mongoloids

Mixed Regions between Mongoloids and Europoids (Caucasoids)

Europoids

Negroids

alone. They could not exchange characteristics with one another, the "flow of genes from group to group was interrupted" (G. Heberer), that means that no mingling of inhabitants followed. The men of the West developed their own differentiation centre just as Southern mankind and the Eastern people had possessed their own central points of separation for ages. Each of these selfcontained spheres was imbued with a special spatial dynamic force: the more progressive peoples in regions favourable to them drove the weaker and less adaptable into the less favourable marginal districts. The stock or peoples who in such slow struggles failed to hold their own "sought escape routes and strongholds of retreat, and evolution rested and was slowed down in the quiet forests and fringing countries." (E. v. Eickstedt). Thus one finds to this day the most ancient primitive races "right outside" — the Veddahs in India and the Malay Peninsula, the Hottentots and Bushmen in South Africa, the Australoids in their remote continent, the Ainus in the Northernmost Japanese Islands. So it was immediately after the beginning of this dynamic process. The Australopithecenes were

chapter and to compare the relief map of the world on pp. 96/97 with the map on pp. 172/173. It is in such a possible area that the three racial masses have probably developed. E. v. Eickstedt propounds a convincing working theory by which the threefold division of the central Asiatic landmass also created the conditions for a threefold division of mankind.

With the beginning of the Ice Age two ice barriers fixed the natural borders firmly: from the Alps to the Himalayas man in the south was locked out from the east as from the west. The ice barrier of the Altai separated the people living to the east from those to the west. Three environs were isolated from one another. Each of the three large groups developed

Fig. 148. Asian racial types:
A Woman from Siberia   B Man from Siberia   C Girl from Northern Mongolia

beaten right to the southern end of the African continent by groups more active and better able to cope, and the Neandertalers on to the European peninsula of the Eurasian continental mass. Animal geography has also observed a similar "radial dynamism": from the same Asiatic primeval native land, of all the mammals; the more primitive groups were driven to the marginal regions by those of a higher organization.

A second query for race history is this, however: how did the further differentiation within the three great races come about. One may imagine something like this:

1. A community which will propagate hominids lives, as gatherer-no-mads, in a prairie which does not offer much to a man who cannot nourish himself on weeds and grasses.

2. The hordes must live divided from one another to avoid poaching on each other's scanty food stocks. Each horde needed a large collecting area and a wide hunting country.

3. So the hordes did not mingle. They lived on by inbreeding. Inherited mutations which occured could rapidly develop in an isolated horde and become typical of that horde. Separate local forms developed which distinguished horde from horde.

4. If a horde or tribe migrated into a collecting district which suited them better and were there exposed

Fig. 149. Asian racial types:
A Girl from Southern India   B Girl from Western China   C Girl from Western China

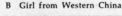

Girl from Southern Mongolia   E Man from Northern India   F Man from Central India

to new and strange demands from their surroundings, then their new environment forced them to alterations. They developed characteristics and qualities which led to a new race.

5. If the climate of the original habitat changed in the course of millennia and they did not migrate then their inherited structure became unbalanced.

6. Restlessness increased if the area of their habitat became restricted by climatic factors and they had to seek new grounds. To new, changed surroundings they had to answer with changes in their physique and spirits. This favoured a variation in breeding and the formation of different races.

7. In propagation communities of the primeval men who inhabited tropical and subtropical prairies the formation of new races was retarded.

8. In the cold periods af the Ice Age the alterations occurred much quicker in the European North as in the Asian North, in regions of the Himalayas as in the Altai, and also in the Glacial age Pluvials of the tropics.

9. The primordial Homo who, either willingly or not, visited these regions, had to adapt himself to these extremes of climate and respond to it by rapid alterations or perish. Certain folks followed — in each successive Interglacial or warm period — the retreating ice

D Japanese   E Japanese woman   F Negroid type from Siam

Fig. 150. Survey map of the distribution of the great races about 1500 A.D.

edges to the northward and fell back to the south with the commencement of a new cold period. Even though the changes from cold to warm periods needed enormous lengths of time in years yet the peoples of Asia and Europe followed the movements of the ice, suffered a change and commenced their wanderings anew.

10. These mass folk migrations produced disturbances even in the communities of propagation, far away from the ice barriers, who were being crowded by the waves of migrants from the North.

11. The Southern folk probably never visited the consistently unfavourable North even during the warm periods. Only the Northern people, who were adapted to the temperate or the polar zones followed the ice or the tundra. The races of the North mixed only to a small extent with those of the South. The Glacial periods bred a special, extreme race with their separate peculiarities.

12. The pressure of the glaciations must have, very early on, driven communities of propagation into regions which were for them quite out of the way and to which they had not climatically been accustomed. Some of them adapted themselves to the new conditions and founded new races.

13. After further millennia sub-races

had been formed by mutations and these eventually became races.

14. Examples: Perhaps Homo steinheimensis was a representative of the palaeo-European macrocephalic race and from him the Northern European and the Mediterranean races may have descended. In similar circumstances, from the Mongoloids have emerged the East mongoloids, the South mongoloids, the Lapps, Malays, and the Turkotatar group.

In Africa, also, such racial differentiations have been worked out. Yet not too much is known about the history of Post-glacial races and populations. The "Dark Continent" was never so dark as has been commonly supposed.

Man, who succeeded in breeding domestic animals from wild, has himself become the most distinctly domestic animal. But only from a certain cultural stage onward has he been subject to the process of "self-domestication". Primeval man was — like the animal's wild form — subject only to nature, which bred him. And when, under such conditions, the primeval races mingled, then this original sort of race formation had nothing to do with the processes which take place in the highly domesticated phase of man. Here man himself encroaches on the prerogative of nature; drives natural breeding to the wall and tries to become the creator and leader of his own bodily and spiritual mutability. Apart from that — since the late Palaeolithic there has been upon earth only Homo sapiens, a single human species in which all individuals can fruitfully interbreed; it is not separated by any restrictions of pairing and fertility. Within this species, Homo sapiens, one can recognise breeding communities, after the late Palaeolithic, which isolated themselves from other

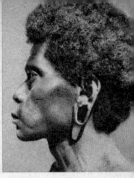

Fig. 151. Oceanian racial types:
A Man from New Caledonia   B Man from Melanesia   C Man from Melanesia

"populations" and are distinguished by special hereditary characteristics which other human groups do not possess -- these are races. They do not stand still and are also not restricted by time. Race is a fluid process, it should be conceived as a process of becoming, or creation, and of an enduring transformation.

The serial illustrations of racial types in this chapter naturally only hold good for the state of affairs at present. The characteristics which distinguish the great races are these: Caucasoid or European: countenance with pronounced features, sleek to somewhat curly hair, narrow, high nose, light skin colour. Mongoloids: flat, median face with low root of the nose, high cheekbones and flat-lying eye openings, heavy eyelids and "mongolian fold", thick, straight, black hair, skin of a yellowish tinge. Negroids: very dark skin, crinkly hair, very broad nose, prognathism and thick lips.

For the uninformed the changes of the past remain invisible. The abundance of present racial types is so great and classification in tabular form of the racial systems is so con-

C Indian woman
from North America
    D Indian from North America
    E Indian from North America

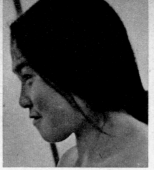

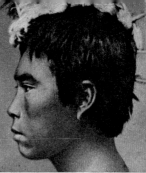

152. Australian racial types: Aborigine

Fig. 153. American racial types: A Polar Eskimo girl

B Indian from North America

fusing and often also contradictory, that an observer, unless he is an expert, regards this "arrangement" without a clue to it.

Investigators are by no means at one on the way to classify a race; by outward characters, colour of the skin, and colour of hair, language, historical descent or after the inherited marks of a breeding community. The race is a member of the species and the individual races are often, but not always, separated by geographical space from one another. There is then, as we saw, besides such races, still higher systematic entities, the

Great races and Lower ones, the sub-races and local forms, which are restricted to a very limited space.

It should also be borne in mind that the racial systems of classification of the savants are very diverse in their details and that the systems cannot always be correlated. Yet when the systematic reviews of the most important experts are compared with one another they coincide in their broader features. In any event, they will not endure. Race classification as a young quasi-science is in a constant flux and new researches and findings demand new arrangements.

lian from Central America

G Indian woman from Central America

H Indian from South America

THE HUMAN HERITAGE
AND REBIRTH

Behind the inflexible forces of our surroundings, terrestial and even extra-terrestrial, which mould us and transform us, there are ruling Powers which first made us pliable and malleable. The outward conditions, the living space, the climate, temperature and humidity of the air; light and the rays we receive are only the stage setting. They seem to have guided the history of man on this planet — but they would accomplish nothing if man did not meet them in so receptive a manner. Only the heritable nature of plants, animals and man, together with the environment comprise the true history of living beings. The "mechanisms of inheritance" are difficult to penetrate since one has to deal with an infinite number of small structures. But a history of man would be incomplete if one did not describe the working and the actions of these often almost abstract structures. If they were kept from the reader only because they are difficult to grasp then it would cheat him of the most profound, most mysterious part of the history of his own genus.

Perhaps once the lower forms of life had issued from the lifeless, then life would renew itself and go on.

Living beings have the ability to multiply and thus life is regenerated by itself. Without propagation life would not continue. Each living being receives its life and its character configuration from a being of the same kind as itself. The species are not moulded firmly for ever, they can alter. From lower or more simply constructed species, more complicated and more highly organised creatures arose.

The alterations were preserved by being inherited. There are two forces, in the first place, which change the species and make from simple organisms more complicated ones.

Spontaneously occuring sudden changes in hereditary characters, that is "mutations" are passed on by further cross-breeding and combine in new ways; and secondly natural selection, the survival of the most adaptable; a silent, interminably long-enduring "struggle for survival". In long-lived organisms hundreds of thousands of years may pass before a "selectional advantage" finds visible expression. Without the presence of mutation and the action of selection, life would never have emerged from its first form; it would not have been able to develop from the simple to the complicated.

The study of the natural development of living beings, the study of evolution, is concerned with the following problems (excepting of course the problem of the origin of the first living things from dead matter): to settle how life multiplies in a sexual or an asexual manner. How the incalculable plenitude of life on our planet with its divergent families, genera and species came to be, how, from existing species, new hereditarily fixed species arise, how it is possible that a living creature should fit into its environment and how it comes to pass, that in the course of time it is transformed into a more complicated figure. The assumption that living beings develop was not at all obvious. The prevailing belief before Lamarck, whose study of descent ("Philosophie Zoo-

"there are as many species as were created at the original beginning." This formula expressed the general world opinion, namely that all organisms were well established from the creation of the world and had thereafter suffered no change. Even Goethe, who is counted amongst the founders of the study of descent, only became acquainted with the idea of evolution during the last

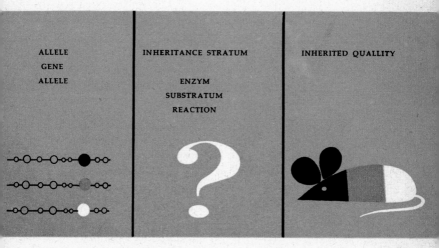

ALLELE
GENE
ALLELE

INHERITANCE STRATUM

ENZYM
SUBSTRATUM
REACTION

INHERITED QUALLITY

Fig. 154. From the genes the material substratum of the inheritance factor and its different forms to the hereditary characteristic and its various expressions there runs a path of which we know a great deal but which we do not understand yet (after Wette).

logique") appeared in 1809, was that at the beginning all species of plants and animals including man, were created by some divine miracle and did not differ in appearance from the present. 200 years ago Linnaeus, in his book "Systema Naturae" included man as a genus of the Primates in nature and in 1750 formulated the original creation in these words:

years of his life. Before that he had been convinced that the graduated similarity of the organisms did not rest on relationships but that the species could be traced back to Platonic "original images".

One could not, after all make experiments with men and the higher animals to prove the evolution of the organisms: they were trans-

A   B

Fig. 155. Adaptation to climate, the cold and heat forms in man and beast are inheritable and have a selective value in the struggle for existence.
A) Desert fox and B) Arctic fox (after Hesse). C) Arab and D) Mongol (after Clauss and v. Eickstedt).

formed and developed only after immense time intervals! Short-lived man could not know of the transformation of his own species. Only when the value of fossils was understood was it possible to understand the development of life during the epochs of the past.

Men of the Renaissance such as Leonardo da Vinci, Frascatore or Palissy had already recognised that fossils were the remains of once living beings. For these men found that they were no "Jokes of Nature" as was then generally believed. But only in the 18th and 19th centuries did men like Fr. v. Schlotheim, Adolphe Theodore Brongiart or Sternberg incorporate the fossil remains into the then existing nomenclature of living plants and animals. With palaeontology the history of life first

began. The extinct organisms were seen as links in a chain of historical developments — a history of the world of the living was opened. Human history was at the same time the last and the shortest chapter of this historical work. And when the fossil remains were compared with Linnaeus' arrangement it showed that the classes, orders and families of the extinct plants and animals had appeared in the same order as they appeared in the natural system which until then included only the living organisms. Living beings had thus developed from the very beginning in the sequence of their organisational level. It is understandable that palaeontology got an immense uplift by the victory of the study of descent. Greek natural philosophers, Immanuel Kant, Erasmus Darwin, the grandfather of Charles Darwin, and finally Jean Baptiste Lamarck, believed in a natural development of living beings. But only Charles Darwin in 1859 created, with his Theory of Selectivity (in his work "On the

C

D

origin of species by natural selection or The surival of the fittest in the struggle for existence") a plausible explanation of organic evolution and one compatible with scientific knowledge. It was a theory, be it noted, which was able to explain the origin of species by natural selection in a struggle or race for existence and the survival of the best adapted. In this same work Darwin sought for a theory which would explain phenomena of inheritance as a basis for the theory of descent, yet he came to grief with his fantastic "Pangenesis-Theory" (see "Origin of Species"). That there was some inheritance of characteristics had long been known as for example to the neolithic animal breeders and later to the Greek natural philosophers, who recommended the employment of the methods of animal breeding.

These succeeded, but only after investigations which, with the help of experiments, developed hypotheses into theories and proved that they could solve the problem — whether a species was unchangeable or mutable. It is not widely known that long before the appearance of Darwin's major work and before the breeding experiments of the Augustine monk, Gregor Mendel, an 18th century botanist, Josef Gottlieb Kolreuter, carried out experiments on the hybridisation of plants and hence was able to prove by experiment that an alteration of the species could occur: at that time this was something unusual, but brought Kolreuter little fame, since a philosopher who merely demonstrated nature with his philosophy of living was more respected than an experimenter. Again it was a German, the physician Karl Friedrich von Gärtner, who in the years 1807 to 1844 carried out experimental research on the sexuality of plants and collected a great mass of observational data on fertilization and hybridisation in plants. Even he was not the first to describe the heritable individual characteristics of a living thing without, however, recognising the law implied by the path of heredity. The French physicist and mathematician, Maupertuis, had uttered similar ideas as long ago as 1745.

The possibility of arriving at well-reasoned conclusions, even without experiments, can be learnt from the works of Ernst Haeckel, the impassioned fighter for the "laws of heredity" formulated by Darwin: "Every organism transmits the same morphological and physiological characteristics, which it inherited, to its own heirs." This was at that time pure conjecture for Mendel's attempts at cross-breeding were only rediscovered and became generally known in 1900. Haeckel's thesis was correct but his theory was false, taken over from Lamarck, according to whom, qualities acquired during the life of an individual are transmitted to the germinal cells and thus passed on to the descendants. Six years after the appearance of "The Origin of Species", Mendel published, in 1865, his "Experiments with plant hybrids". They appeared in the transactions of the "Natur-forschenden Verein" (Nature Research Society) of Brünn and were not at first noticed, although his findings were, for biology, of the most revolutionary importance. Seven long years he spent in the Foundation garden of the monastery at Brünn (whose Abbot he later became) carrying out and describing well over 10,000 plant hybridization experiments with beans and peas. Mendel did not himself lay down any laws of inheritance and only suggested the processes which take place when characteristics are transmitted from one generation to the next. For 55 years one of the most important texts of the new natural science remained unevaluated. Only in 1900 were the "Mendelian Laws" evolved, derived by C. Correns, E. Tschermak and H. de Vries independently, from the facts which Mendel hat produced and arranged in such a masterly manner.

Three laws of heredity crystalized from Mendel's experiments: the law of uniformity, the law of division and the law of independence. Simplifying, one may say: Homogeneous or pure breeds are pure races. The heirs resemble their parents in all respects. They breed true thereafter.

If two races of one species, which are distinguishable from one another, are crossed, then their descendants appear essentially the same outwardly. If characters are dominant, the offspring resemble one of their parents, being that parent with the dominant character. In the intermediary path of heredity the potentiality of both parents will be valid equally and produce a picture which apparently lies between the parental characteristics (intermediate hybrids).

Should two distinguishable purebred races of a species be crossed then their descendants are mixed but superficially alike.

If the resulting cross-breeds are then crossed with each other the parental characters again separate. The heritage splits up, and this division occurs in certain fixed numerical proportions.

Here we must distinguish between the apparent picture produced (the phenotype) formed by the interplay of hereditary attributes (the genotype), and environmental influence and the genotype itself. The phenotype and the genotype are determined by the pattern of the hereditary

Mendel's greatest service lies in the fact that he recognised the fractionality and particularity of the inheritance factors. In the bodies and primordial sex cells in higher organisms, each of these particular hereditary factors are present exactly twice. This diploid set, however, is reduced

Fig. 156. The golden hamster is easily kept as a pet. In the larger broods hereditary jump-changes occur off and on, the mutations; on left: albinoid golden hamster; right: normal golden hamster.

characters. Genotypically identical individuals, for instance, the brothers resulting from a cross of two pure lines, can present more or less different phenotypes if they are reared in different environments. But individuals with different genotypes can have the same, or nearly the same, phenotypes as, for example 3/4ths of the descendants of the 2nd hybrid generation where one of his grand parents had certain dominant characters and the other recessive characters (see Fig. 159).

during the formation or maturation of the germ cells to a single or haploid set. When the ovum or female germ cell is fertilized by the male germ cell or spermatozoon, the two haploid sets are united into a renewed diploid basic set. This consists, therefore of a single set from each of the mating partners (in the figures a female is designated by the sign of Venus ♀ and a male by the sign of Mars ♂). In the maturation divisions leading to the formation of the germ cells by the process of meiotic division no optical difference can be detected between the maternal and the paternal sets. But each germ cell of an individual of the first offspring of the filial generation, designated by F₁ will contain maternal as well as

Pure bred individuals possess two identical sets of heritage complements in all instances and give rise in succeeding generations to a pure line. The hybrids (F₁) created by the crossing of two pure bred races (in the P generation) are therefore genotypically alike and, with the same environment, will be alike phenotypically (1st Mendelian law). But because of the independence of the paternal and maternal complements in meiosis these can combine freely in the next (the F₂) generation and therefore give rise to several genotypes and the phenotypes corresponding to them. This 2nd Mendelian law was first shown to be only for a single characteristic but Mendel later examined the pattern of simultaneous inheritance of several different characteristics in one individual with the results combined in his 3rd law: that simultaneously several characteristics or their basic heritage complements will combine independently and divide.

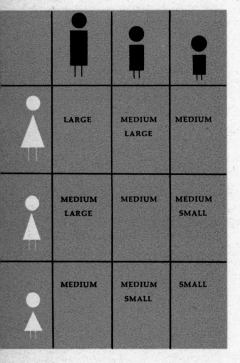

Fig. 157. The size of a man is decided by many factors of inheritance and thus shows smooth transitions influenced by environment (after Wette).

paternal complements (of the parental generation designated by a P). The same holds good for the following generations of descendants (F₂) and so on.

Since the processes of inheritance recognised by Mendel have validity not only for plants but for all organisms, including animals and man, their results are of universal importance. Mendel knew nothing of chromosomes and genes (see below), he was unable to foresee that the material nature of the chromosomes and genes would one day be proved, and at least the chromosomes would be made visible. Modern genetics and cytology (the study of cells) confirmed the Mendelian laws. Experimental genetics and the parallel cytological experiments have, in the course of five decades, laid down the mechanics of the pattern of inheritance exactly and clearly and they have also provided a precise insight into the structure of the entire inheritance complement of a living being. Each plant, every animal and naturally man also, possesses a certain number of chromosomes which are characteristic of each species and remain so. Each human body-cell, for instance, contains 46 chromosomes which are arranged in two sets each of 23; the mouse, on the other hand, possesses 40 chromosomes, the cebus monkey 54, the fruit fly Drosophila (with which the most important genetical experiments were carried out) only 4, the scarlet runner bean 12 and maize 20. It is interesting that the chromosome numbers in man and chimpanzee and in other Old World monkeys are the same. The normal chromosomes are rod shaped, V shaped and J shaped.

In re-examining the 3rd Mendelian law it appeared, surprisingly, that

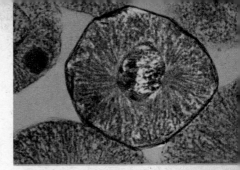
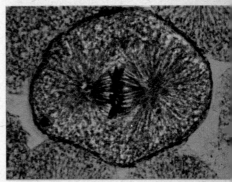

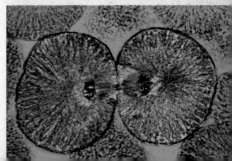

Fig. 158. The usual cell and nucleus division or Mitosis. From the top: 1. Spiralisation and the contraction connected with it of the double sets of chromosomes, spindle formation issuing from centrosome and dissolution of the nuclear membrane — 'Prophase'. 2. Spindle formation completed and the arranging of the chromosomes which have meanwhile split from the equatorial plate round the spindle (profile view) — 'Metaphase'. 3. The chromosome halves are drawn by the spindle fibres of the spindle along the spindle into the future daughter cells, each contains a complete set of two chromosomes — 'Anaphase'. 4. Dissolution of the spindle, cell division, uncoiling of the chromosomes and reforming of the nucleus membrane — 'Telophase'.

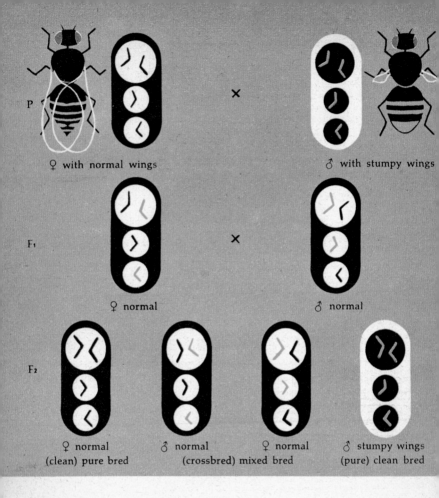

P ♀ with normal wings   ✕   ♂ with stumpy wings

F₁ ♀ normal   ✕   ♂ normal

F₂
♀ normal (clean) pure bred   ♂ normal (crossbred) mixed bred   ♀ normal (crossbred) mixed bred   ♂ stumpy wings (pure) clean bred

Fig. 159. The first two Mendelian laws (Uniformity and Division laws) in a dominant-recessive hereditary path: in the Drosophila fruit fly the normal characteristic form is "long winged". Above: the two pure bred parent animals (P — generation). Middle: 1 filial gener-ation (F₁) with uniform long wings (1st Mendelian law). Below: 2. Filial generation by crossing of the F₁ animals with one another: Division in the proportions of 3:1 (1 pure bred and 2 cross bred longwinged, 1 pure bred stumpy animal — 2nd Mendelian law). The large circles symbolise the diploid somatic cells, the small ones the haploid germinal cells with the chromosomes which carrythe alleles for the characteristic form "long winged" or "stumpy wings" (after Wette).

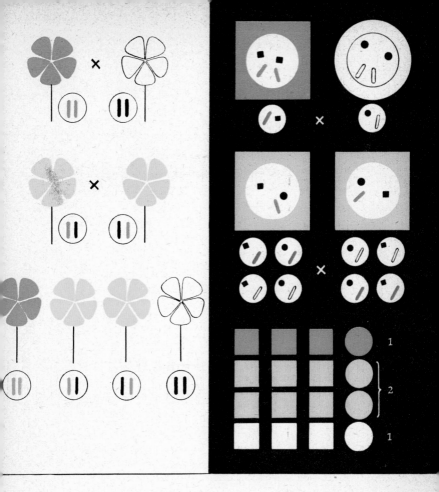

Fig. 160. The 1st and 2nd Mendelian laws in intermediary inheritance. F₁ (median) lies between the two parents (P generation see above) and divides, crossed with each other, in the F₂ generation (below) in the proportion of 1 pure bred, 2 of mixed heritage, 1 pure bred. Here the two parental phenotypes (1 + 1) and the F₁ type (2×) crop up. The germinal cells are not indicated here.

Fig. 161. The 3rd Mendelian law (diagrammatic) with two characteristics with a) dominant recessive inheritance ("edged" dominant over "round") and b) median inheritance of colour. Top and middle: 1st Mendels law (see previous illustrations). Below: 2nd and 3rd Mendels law: Independent division of the two characteristics in the proportion of 3:1 and 1:2:1 (Figs 159, 160, 161 after Wette),

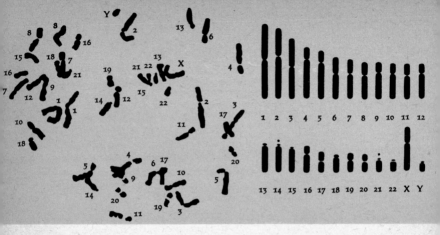

Fig. 162. Chromosome set of a skin cell of a newly born boy, from a tissue culture. Enlarged 1120 fold. Each chromosome is characterised by a certain size and form. It can also be seen clearly that each chromosome consists of two parallel-lying halves. Next to it an 'ideogram' of a simple male chromosome set. At end the two sexual chromosomes X and Y (redrawn after Chu).

certain characteristics, or their corresponding hereditary complements, can be more or less coupled together. For example, a complementary couple makes itself apparent, either by two characters which do not split up or recombine freely like other characters, or their separation takes place less often than would be expected if the characters were independent. These characters which do not conform to the 3rd Mendelian law are called "linked" and are collected together in linkage groups.

When the body forms the sex cells, (the ova and sperms) then in the maturation division the double set of chromosomes divides into two halves. Every sperm cell and egg cell, therefore, contains only one set of chromosomes which is derived either entirely from only one of the parents or else it contains a mixture of chromosomes from both parents. By

the union of egg and sperm cells there forms a combination of the parental chromosomes. The fertilized egg divides into two cells. These again split and thus matters proceed through innumerable divisions. Before a cell divides the chromosomes also divide, they halve along their major axis and the two halves split equally with a wonderful precision. Both the cells then possess an equal chromosome complement.

In the chromosomes there are numerous active entities which theory requires as carriers of the hereditary properties: they are the factors of heredity or genes, and have not yet been seen by human eyes. After many trials we know their activities and after numerous experiments we can also say that the nature of the material they consist of has been proved: in 1949 the Americans, Schultz and Lawrence found nodule-like thicken-

Fig. 163. Microphotographs of a giant chromosome — consisting to a certain extent of many single chromosomes stuck together and stretched — out of a salivary gland cell of a midge (in section). The individual bands of corresponding chromomeres of an ordinary chromosome. On left above the (diagrammatic) diploid chromosome set of a Drosophila fruit fly with rod-shaped X and J shaped Y chromosomes.

ings in human chromosomes arranged in linear form. Either these are the already known "chromomeres" or are themselves the genes, or they indicate the positions of the genes and show their number and arrangement. The Drosophila fruit fly, and the maize plant are particularly favourable objects of experiment because on their chromosomes the chromomeres can be easily recognised and identified: the structure of their genotype — the total of its hereditary complement — can be precisely analysed.

If in meiosis the chromosomes of a chromosome pair cross over — and this has also been observed in human cells — then homologous parts of chromosomes are exchanged. Through this it became possible to produce detailed chromosome charts for Drosophila melanogaster, in which a long series of genes which were

responsible for certain characteristics like hairy winged, small winged or small eyed, and so on, were plotted. In the giant chromosomes (of the salivary gland cells in Drosophila larvae) a consecutive series of segments, or rather formations of a dot and dash shaped nature can be observed. Even if they do not actually represent the genes, they may at least indicate the places where the genes exist. At the International Congeress for Genetics in 1958 electron microscopic photographs were displayed which showed these heritage-carriers of Drosophila, of bacteria and of viruses. In the chromosome photographs septa could be seen which consisted of fibrils running parallel to each other.

An estimate may be made of the number of genes (and thus of his inherited characteristics) for man with his 23 chromosome pairs.

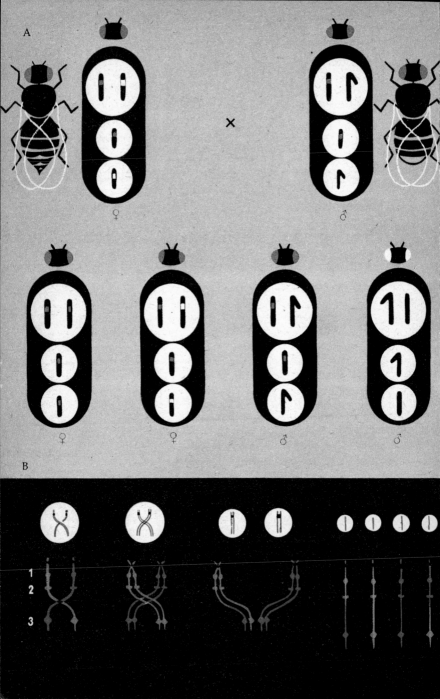

If it is assumed that in each single chromosome one thousand genes lie concealed, then man possesses $2 \times 23{,}000$ genes. By comparitive cytology and genetical examination it was possible to prove that in the chromosomes numerous active units are coupled together which must be bearers of the heritage.

In mass breeding carried out over generations of pure bred animals or plants, spontaneous and irregular heritable characteristics occurred, whose bearers are called mutants; this had long been known to breeders before Darwin's day (the "sports" of English horse and dog breeders.) The process itself is called mutation and the mutants created by mutation can be bred on as pure breeds. It turned out that a mutation is the transition at one bound of an here-

ditary factor or gene from one condition to another. The hereditary factor responsible for a certain characteristic can therefore occur in several forms, which are designated allelomorphic genes or heritage factors, or simply as alleles. One gene can therefore occur in the form of two or several alleles (simple or multiple alleles) but it must be remembered that in the diploid body and premeiotic cells only two alleles either different or alike can be represented simultaniously.. The different alleles of the same genes, are those therefore, which cause a certain character to occur in various forms. Whether a certain character is dominant over another, intermediate with it or combinantly inheritable depends on the particular nature of the allelic gene-partner and on their relation to one another. The change of a single gene can act so powerfully that it can influence the whole development of an individual. This altered gene can encroach so strongly on the course of the individual's life that the individual dies from internal causes. These are the so-called lethal genes (and the lethal factors required by them). They destroy the individual who carries them, for they are duplicate (from the father and the mother united). Nowadays medical genetics recognises these lethal characteristics and can, for instance, study them in infantile amaurotic idiocy. From the presence of lethal genes one can understand the vital importance of each single gene in the course of the development of a living being.

Fig. 164 A. Fixing the sex and sexual linkage of the inheritance in the Drosophila fruit fly through (rod-shaped) X and J shaped Y chromosomes. XX — individuals are female (♀) XY individuals male (♂). A non-normal recessive allele — e. g. for white skin — lying in one of the two X chromosomes of the mother has already penetrated the male F₁ half. The hereditary path of the sex coupled haemophilia in man, for instance, runs precisely in a corresponding manner (after Wette).

Fig. 164 B. In the chromosomes linked genes do not follow Mendels 3rd law if they lie close enough together (close or absolute linkage (1 and 2). In the meiosis the parts resulting from a chromosome division may break and undergo a "wrong" recombination — the further apart they are the more easily it can happen (2 and 3). An exchange of factors is involved in such a "crossing over", and Mendels 3rd law will only be broken gradually (after Wette).

Sexual processes fertilize the germ cells and make it possible by reduction division (Meiosis) for new germ cells to be created. If from every mother cell four cells are made then the genes therein contain once the parental genotype and for the other the parental genotype in a *new* combination. These new types are called "re-combinants". Re-combinants have no purpose for the organism except to satisfy the individual's sexual urge. The actual value of sexuality, and therefore of the re-combinants, lies outwardly, above the existence of the individual organism ... it multiplies to a certain extent the type number being created by mutation and thereby hastens evolution. For the same reason the plant and animal breeder uses "crossing", that is, the pairing of two races to obtain from them new races.

By the genotype of an individual is meant the pattern of his genetic complement, that is, the pattern of the pairs of alleles represented in his cells. In parenthesis be it said that naturally not all genes have to be represented, each by two different alleles, but that a certain fraction of all genes may be represented each by an allele in duplicate. Jn absolutely pure stock this is true for all genes, that is, they possess two identical complements or sets. The genotype

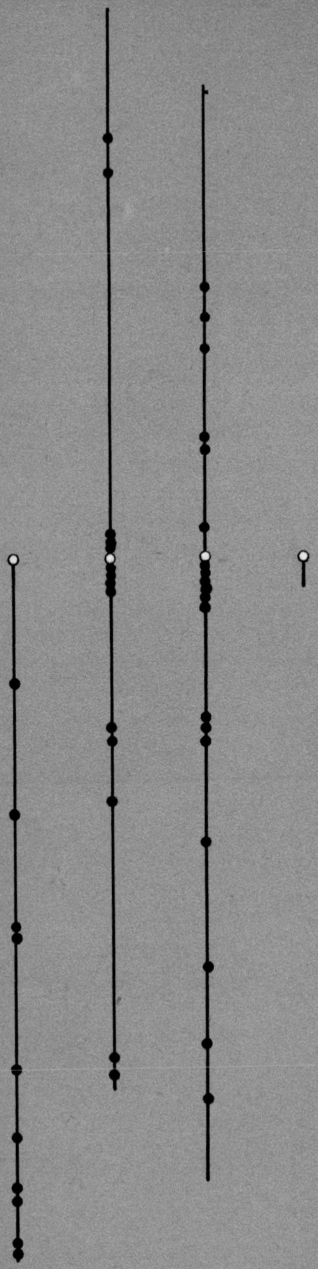

Fig. 165. The linear arrangement of the genes in the genetical chromosome charts of the fruit fly, Drosophila: In three of the four chromosomes some gene positions responsible for the colour of the eyes are drawn in (after Wette).

of an individual, then, determines his reaction norm (Woltereck), the range within which the characteristic mould, the phenotype of genetically identical individuals in different environmental circumstances can move. Since hitherto we have simply discussed characteristics and complements, we must now identify these conceptions more precisely. A characteristic like, for example, the colour of the hair can be realised in many variations and in various forms. The hereditary characteristics or hereditary qualities have hereditary complements as their bases which are a hithero unknow, but theoretically valuable hypothetical principle. By reason of the divisibility of the hereditary complement already found by Mendel these are traced back to hereditary factors, or genes.

Certainly, by no means all, actually only very few characteristics are determined by only one gene (= monogenic) most are determined by several (called the multifactorial transmission of hereditary characters or polygeny); equally many, or even most, hereditary factors or genes have a simultaneous share in several characteristics (pleiotropy or polypheny). Yet it is precisely the rarer instances of monogenic inheritance which gave us the first and deepest insight into the action of inheritance. All this, however, could only be perceived when biology had investigated the "elementary particles" of living substance, the cells and their contents.

The marvellous adventure of the voyage into the interior of the cell be-

gan in 1831. A Scottish botanist, Robert Brown (who also discovered the Brownian molecular movement named after him) observed, with the help of the improved microscope, a spherical body which he christened the nucleus, the nucleus of the cell.

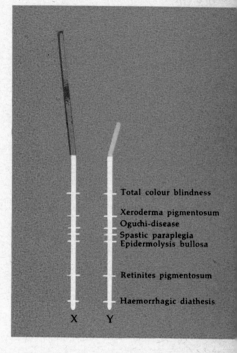

Total colour blindness

Xeroderma pigmentosum
Oguchi-disease
Spastic paraplegia
Epidermolysis bullosa

Retinites pigmentosum

Haemorrhagic diathesis

X   Y

Fig. 166. The sex chromosomes of man show a homologous piece (white) corresponding to the autosome. The incompletely sexually bound inheritable diseases have their gene position, which it has even been possible to determine approximately — In the non-homologous long portion of the X-chromosome (gray) there lie the sexually linked inheritance-factors and diseases; in the non-homologous part of the Y-chromosome (green) the (holandric) inheritance factors and diseases occuring only in man (redrawn after Snyder).

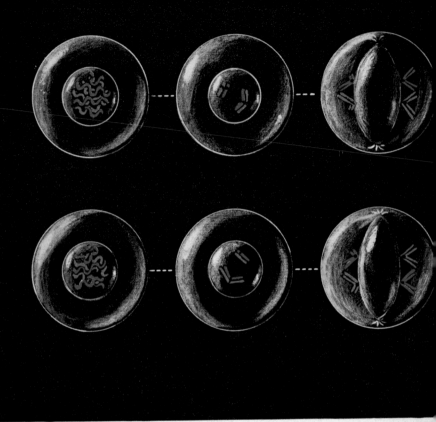

Fig. 167. The maturation divisions in the formation of the germinal cells (meiosis). Left to right: 1. "fatherly" (blue) and "motherly" (red) chromosomes lying in the diploid nucleus. 2. Pairing of the strongly spiralized homologous chromosomes. 3. Increasing the distance between homologous chromosomes in the act of division along the spindle and 4. Their division at random (compare above with below): reduction division to a single chromosome set. 5. Division and 6. consequent equal division of the chromosomes to haploid (each containing a single chromosome) germinal cells (after Wette).

He was the first man to see this structure inside the cell of a plant. It was reserved for a rival of Darwin's who had conceived a separate theory of genealogy, the botanist Carl Wilhelm Naegeli, to determine the existence of even smaller basic units of the cell. He asserted that in the living cell during certain phases or cycles of the cell nucleus a whole series of much smaller bodies became visible. A versatile biologist,

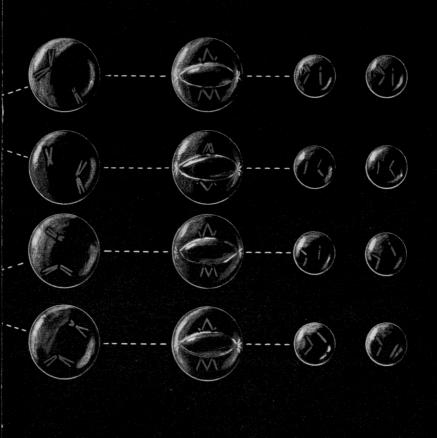

Wilhelm v. Waldeyer-Hartz, who had written a book on "Der Eierstock und das Ei" ("The ovary and the Egg") named Naegeli's cell nuclear bodies "chromosomes" (colour bodies from chroma = colour and soma = body) because they took pigment readily when being stained for slides under the microscope. Incidentally, it may be remarked that Naegeli who actually found Mendel's carrier of inheritance, was corresponding with Mendel on

questions of inheritance, and did not even acknowledge him.

O. Hertwig, a pupil of Haeckel's, made an outstanding discovery in 1875 whilst on a voyage of study in the Mediterranean area. He showed that fertilization comes about by a combination of the ovum and the spermatozoon cells and in particular of egg nucleus with the sperm nucleus, and that there was a process of maturation division in the male pro-

209

duction of germ cells whereby their chromosome complement is reduced to half.

Hertwig also turned against Darwin. At the age of seventy-two he declared that the part of the Darwinian Theory which postulated "The struggle for existence" was a coincidental theory, but admitted that the study of 'Origin' was otherwise valid. Perhaps he had been a victim of the German translators who of "struggle" had made "fight", whereas Darwin very conscientiously distinguished between "struggle" and "war" or "fight".

In Hertwig's work "Das Werden der Organismen" ("The origin of the organisms") which he published in 1889 there is the important sentence "all cells of an organism are, through the possession of the same ideoplasm, bearers of the qualities of the species and only become differentiated into tissue and organ cells because during the process of development they come under the influence of various conditions and by the law of the division of labour some carry out particurlar functions better than the remainder and are therefore differentiated also in their structure."

Thus there arose, even in the second half of the last century, a distinct suspicion that the chromosomes in the cell nucleus are the material transmitters of inherited characteristics. The "mendelizing" of human inherited characteristics is incapable of analysis if several genes are to be made responsible for one characteristic — and such polygeny is

normal. Nature, has, however, provided investigators with a lasting and continuous grand experiment: the formation of twins. Even if in research into twins, no genes can be directly analyzed yet the fact of their being twins provides the material to prove that in man also a hereditary character is transmitted by hereditary factors.

There are, as is well known, genuine mono-zygotic and di-zygotic twins. Mono-zygotic twins occur from one fertilized ovum, through the division of the germinal layer in an early stage of development. They have the same inherited characteristics and are always af the same sex. The di-zygotic twins develop from two simultaneously or consecutively fertilized eggs. They are also of the same age but, like all normal brothers and sisters, are hereditarily like or unlike, and may be of different sexes. It is valuable for research into twins to compare the characteristics of mono- and di-zygotic twins. They are a sure method to determine whether inheritance genes take part in the development of a characteristic. For human or domestic animal geneticists they are substitutes for an otherwise insoluble problem, namely an experiment on "pure" lines of descent to investigate their mutability. As V. Verschuer remarked "It is an infallible method." All differences in di-zygotic twins of the same sex which exceed the measure stabilised for mono-zygotic twins are determined by inheritance. In this manner first proof has been obtained of the demands of the requirements of heredity in a great number of human qualities, especially in the more complicated hereditary ones and those depending on environmental influences. As an example, let us take the genetics of some minor human morphological characteristics, the shape of ears, hands, feet and cutaneous ridges which can be observed and analyzed in living people.

ridges of the hand and foot surfaces and finally in the finger pads ("finger prints").

"One of the show pieces of the biology of heredity in man is the genetics of the blood", wrote Professor Schwidetzky. The blood groups depend upon antibodies which are required by heredity. In different heritable blood characteristics there are diverse albumen structures to which there is

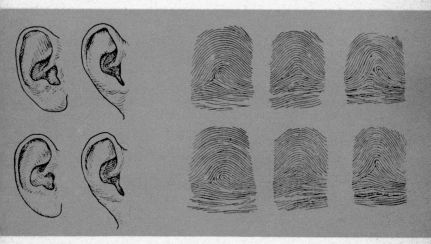

Fig. 168. The morphologically finer (or minor) human characteristics may be seen in the living body and analysed. The investigation on twins especially enriched genetical studies which follow the mould of inheritance of human bodily form. In the picture are, left, the ears of monozygote twins, those of the first twin above, and those of the second below. The right side of the picture shows how much the similarities are emphasised in monozygotic twins. Here are the cutaneous ridges of the finger pads of the index, middle and ring finger of the right hand in monozygotic twins. Above those of the first and below those of the second twin (drawings after photos by Abel and Lotze).

The similarities of fold formations in the eye, the shape of the lips, wrinkling the brow or the ways and means of imitating formations of folds in laughing, are particularly impressive. Mendelian hereditary layers are directly visible in the fine cutaneous

direct access from the genes. In a blood serum the red corpuscles are divided up and with it form the blood. The blood serum of certain human groups possesses the quality of clotting the red corpuscles of other human groups into balls.

MOTHER			A		AB	B		O
			AO	AA		BB	BO	
			O A	A A	A B	B B	B O	O O
A	AO	O	OO AO	AO AO	AO BO	BO BO	BO OO	OO OO
		A	AO AA	AA AA	AA AB	AB AB	AB AO	AO AO
	AA	A	AO AA	AA AA	AA AB	AB AB	AB AO	AO AO
		A	AO AA	AA AA	AA AB	AB AB	AB AO	AO AO
AB		A	AO AA	AA AA	AA AB	AB AB	AB AO	AO AO
		B	BO AB	AB AB	AB BB	BB BB	BB BO	BO BO
B	BB	B	BO AB	AB AB	AB BB	BB BB	BB BO	BO BO
		B	BO AB	AB AB	AB BB	BB BB	BB BO	BO BO
	BO	B	BO AB	AB AB	AB BB	BB BB	BB BO	BO BO
		O	OO AO	AO AO	AO BO	BO BO	BO OO	OO OO
O		O	OO AO	AO AO	AO BO	BO BO	BO OO	OO OO
		O	OO AO	AO AO	AO BO	BO BO	BO OO	OO OO

Fig. 169. The blood groups of the ABO system: Example of a qualitative inheritance characteristic in man. The three alleles A, B & O yield, in free combination of the 4 groups of parents, 6 different diploid genotypes (AB, AC etc.) but again only 4 different phenotypes (A, AB, B & O) in the children, since A and B are combinant with each other and both are dominant over O (O = nil), after Wette.

There are thus clottable antigenes in the red corpuscles to be distinguished from the clotting antibodies in the blood serum. There are the antigenes "anti A" and "anti B" which clot the red corpuscles with A or B properties.

The blood group of a man is called after the clotting reactions of his red corpuscles and they are O, A, B, and AB. The hereditary factors of both parents took part in forming the hereditary characteristics. A man of the O blood group thus inherited this property of his blood from both his parents and the inheritance picture is O/O. A is dominant; a man of blood group A can therefore possess the hereditary factors A/A or also A/O. The same may be said of B, but a man with blood group AB inherited A from one of his parents and B from the other. Every man retains during his lifetime the bloodgroup peculiar to him.

Here we have reproduced only the original "classic" blood groups. They have been increased during the last decades by subdivision and further antigenes were found, that is, Mendelian clotting characteristics which

man retains also, like all hereditary characteristics, during his life. Since, however, 56 different phenomena of blood characteristics have already been discovered and new ones are continually being added which make possible over 300,000 combinations of types, it is by no means exaggerated to speak of a hereditary individuality of the blood.

Since it is known that man is subject to the laws of heredity and that he has also changed by the gra-

Fig. 170. The blood groups are determined by "clotting reactions". The red blood corpuscles of certain human groups clot into lumps if they are placed together with blood serum from other human groups. There are clottable antigenes in the red blood corpuscles and clotting antibodies in blood serum (after Stern).

Group	Antigene in the red blood cells	Antibody in the serum	Reaction to Serum of red blood cells of the groups			
			O	A	B	AB
O	O	Anti—A Anti—B				
A	A	Anti—B				
B	B	Anti—A				
AB	AB	—				

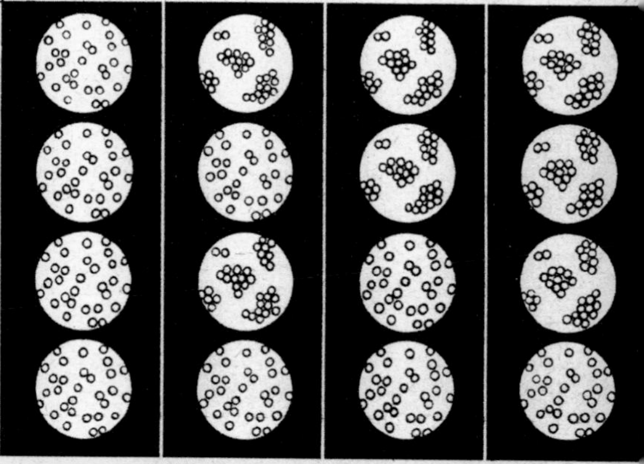

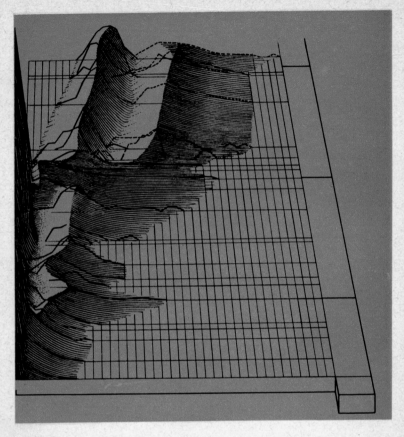

Fig. 171. Panorama of a changing species and separation of a foraminifera group in the course of 7 million years (m. y.). Left, the Gaudryina stock soars as a steep ridge-like rock wall. From it splits the progressive side branch like a spur, separated from the main original stock by a valley. Valley and spur lose themselves in a wide shallow declivity corresponding to the great width of the variation of spiroplectinata. On this declivity almost immediately follow the two spiroplectinata branches which rise as two parallel mountain chains. This foraminifera group which is constantly expanding and unfolding issued from a single original species (after Grabert and Bettenstaedt).

dual alteration of his heritage through various forms to the present Homo sapiens — then the central question must arise in a history of man: how can one imagine such a change in the species and formation of a genus. There is no question here of the creation and alteration of a single individual, not even of a clan with a long line of descent, but of a large propagation community. Such a total stock of individual beings of one species which inhabits a very restricted space, one calls a population. Population genetics deal not only with the problem of the creation of races but also with the question of the formation of species and genera. One ought to realise, in reviewing a history of mankind, that in the frighteningly incomplete state of palaeontological discoveries of anthropoid apes and ape-men, and even of primeval men, original men and ancient men, it is not possible to follow definite lines of development. A huge gap of no less than 15 million years gaped, even from the finding of Proconsul and of the Dryopithecines. Never was a divergent species confirmed or even recognised by fossil discoveries, namely the point in a genealogical scheme at which a certain species clearly separated from the others — further to develop into a new species or family.

By reason of collateral branches which became extinct without continuing their development (and such species have been found in fossil form), one must reasonably, in theory, assume the existence of a species which at some given point of time separated from the extinct species. Neither in the Hominoidaea nor in any other group of animals has there been an unbroken sequence of populations backed by palaeontological discoveries — and this is not to be wondered at, indeed, when one has

to presume that such metamorphoses in species and separations of species stretch over several million years.

Although we are here dealing with the history of mankind we can in this instance look elsewhere than to man because the laws of inheritance work so well and the further formation of species and genera are universal. Can one in any group of animals — or in plants — clear up the problems, by fossil finds, which were brought up at the beginning of this review, for then the factors of evolution for man are clarified — namely, how from firmly formed species new species arise, who, in their turn, transmit their heritage, and how it is possible that a living being can sensibly fit into his environment and how, in the course of time, he changes into a figure with a higher organisation.

A quite extraordinary circumstance has contributed during the last few years to the solution of this very pressing problem. The petroleum industry urged scientists all over the world to examine microfossils, which had been recovered from deep borings. With the determination of the form and position of the stratum of the microfossils the geological age of the strata themselves could be exactly determined. In one kilogramme of rock there are often to be found 10,000 to 20,000 habitations of these microscopically small lodgers, Foraminifera — or Ostracodae, which play a very material part in raising the ocean bottoms.

110 million years ago North-West Germany as far as the central mount-

ains was covered by the sea. The oceanic ooze deposits have now solidified into clay and marl and a 500 metre deep unbroken series of layers was brought up by deep borings. The rocky bore cores were full of an uninterrupted sequence of generations of Foraminifera, which in the course of seven million years had lived there consecutively. Dr. B. Grabert submitted in 1959 her genaelogical investigations into the development of a foraminifera group. At the beginning of this seven million year long evolution the Foraminifera Gaudryina possessed a constricted, pyramidal, three line chambered shell. At the end of seven million years of history a completely new genus, Spiroplectinata, had arisen from it with four different species. It was equipped with an often five fold greater, long and flat shell furnished with a two-line arrangement of chambers. The transitions proceeded gradually, the metamorphoses were smooth and there were no jump changes (mutations) in development.

The original form of Gaudryina lived upon the muddy sea bottom and fed on sinking plankton. With its clumsy figure and its three line chambers it sank deeper into the mud than the later Gaudryina variants or even, perhaps, than the Spiroplecainata with their flat lengthy house and chambers of only two lines. These did not sink so deeply, could support themselves on the surface of the ooze and received a greater mass of food. In the race between the fellow species of a population the plump forms were squeezed out and the "modern", more highly organized species with their superiority in form overran the sea bottom. The shell alterations rest upon mutations. Easily mutable, labile genes call forth changes in heredity which are nearly always harmful or even fatal to the organism. By chance and without plan a hereditary characteristic will be hit upon. At some time or other, however, a mutation amongst thousands serves to the creatures' benefit. Then an uninterrupted period for selection has by chance allowed a suitable object to survive and facilitated the mutant's way and allowed it to reproduce and multiply.

The Gaudryina variants handicapped in their struggle for existence by their heritage of plumpness vanished from the population — an entire community slowly altered and a historic change of species was prepared. A divergence of species, however, is quite a different matter. When several communities of propagation occupy a certain area then there is always the possibility of a reverse crossing. In that case a species can change but not diverge. Only when a spatial division takes place (Isolation), when a community of propagation becomes isolated, can local races arise, which in their stock of genes differ somewhat from the others.

The smaller a population the more strongly does chance take a hand; for mutations are coincidences which serve to either the advantage or detriment, to disappearance or increase of the population.

Fig. 172. Panorama for the theory of selection (after Ludwig). The figures denote the following arguments: 1) Should a race exist on the slopes of an unoccupied peak, if its population is N. in number and if the corresponding mutations occur then it will gradually reach the summit. 2) Should it be in a depression between two or more unoccupied peaks then it can easily split into separate races which begin to climb different peaks. 3) Should a species already be in occupation of a summit and either the mutability increases or the pressure of selectivity diminishes then it will spread down hill or in the event of an opposite change it will withdraw to the uppermost peak. 4) If the environment changes either in climate or the composition of the community then the whole range of hills will suffer constant deformations. The summit upon which hitherto a most suitable species sat can gradually alter i. e. sink so that gradually the species gets into a valley and is in danger of dying out unless by means of mutation they find a way to another summit (which has meanwhile perhaps arisen). 5) If the population N. is very small, chance will determine the outcome. No such species can, for instance, even without a change of environment, descend a mountain, reach a valley, think up some allele or other on the way and lastly climb another peak — yet owing to its smallness it is in constant danger of extinction on the way. (6) If of medium size a population seldom meets with such adventure but the species can "meander about" and finally, unless it dies out before, change over to another summit — (shortened text after Ludwig).

With the following four factors of evolution, metamorphosis in species and divergence of species can be understood: Mutation, Selection, Isolation and Chance.

With this example very drastically simplified but taking a wide view, we have desisted from depicting the dramatic and involved course of the evolutionary story of these Foraminifera in all its detail. To be able to prove it, 60 populations with 18,000 dwellings and, with the assistance of variation statistics, would have had to be counted and plotted in a system of co-ordinates (a graph).

With the newest scientific disciplines, the population genetics and micropalaeontology (which had otherwise nothing to with the investigation) the bases and elementary re-

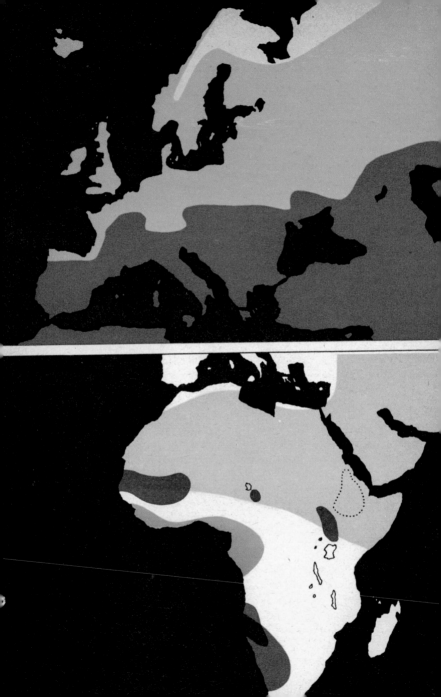

presentations of the study of descent can be made visible in a plastic picture. The otherwise abstract "variation curves" become in this instance, for example, in Dr. Grabert's relief picture of the revolution, an expressive picture of the history of evolution of two Foraminifera species (see fig. 171, p. 214).

Fig. 173. In this can be seen very clearly the relations between the colour of the skin and the action of ultra violet rays in Europe and Africa. In snow-covered countries with strong reflected light a yellow and brown or yellow-brown skin colour forms: in a very cloudy climate as, for instance in Iceland and Scotland, blond colour predominates. In a cloudy misty climate blond and brunet develop and in a strong sun and blue skies a dark brunet (redrawn after Fleure).

Snowcovered with strong reflected light = yellow brown skin

Northerly: Very cloudy = blond
Southerly: Cloudy = blond and brunet

Strong sun and blue skies = darker brunet

Fig. 174. The map of Africa depicts pigmentation from brown to the darkest skin, which stands in very close relation to ultra violet light. The gray shaded areas show the regions of darkest skin colour (redrawn after Fleure).

Strong sun and blue skies

Clouds in summer

Heat, clouds, rain = dark chocolate coloured skin

Strong sun and dry air

When one wishes to indicate the "origin" of the whole of past and present organisms on the basis of the theory of selection, that is, as a selection of the best-adapted beings in a struggle for existence then it cannot be denied and one must admit: such a development was, and is, subject to chance. A selection which alters or splits species cannot function without mutation. If mutants appear, by chance, which show an advantage over selection, one must not say, in spite of that, that selection proceeds blindly. "Chance is the collaboration of many small and, in detail, uncontrollable things." The picture of the living being which becomes visible to us from past and present is only a small segment from all possibilities which under the same conditions as the original beginning of all life on earth might have become true. "Had we a complete picture of the genealogy of all animals and plants which exist on earth and have existed, then it would be shown that that contains not only many branches ending blindly in consequence of the extinction of their groups, but is also studded all over with tiny additions to such branches which have simply never unfolded." (W. Ludwig).

If a living being possesses 1,000 genes and each gene has two to ten alleles then the number of possible inheritance genes together of an organism would exceed the number of all electrons in the world. Only the least quantity of them is realised and even far fewer are capable of living.

Among the genotypes which succeeded in breaking through are to be
understood, however, the genotypes
of an entire order of animals or
family of plants and hence a great
circle of relations.

Professor Ludwig imagined the
following representation: 2^{1000} are
shown as points on a plane surface
which really should be a thousand-
dimensional space — and so that the
closer neighbours to each other two

Fig. 175. The distribution of dwarf growth
(Mean for men · below 148 cm, o 148 cm to
158 cm) — The "pygmies" of Africa, Asis and
the South Seas do not belong to a single
race. The same and similar environment, the
same mutations in the various places on
earth led to dwarfage. Yet the dwarfs are
not inter-related; they are probably parallel
developments which do not, however, grow
from the same roots. The pygmy conception
should only apply to the African dwarf
people of the Congo primeval forest (redrawn after Schwidetzky).

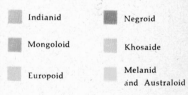

Indianid	Negroid
Mongoloid	Khosaide
Europoid	Melanid and Australoid

Fig. 176. To the methods of anthropology
belong besides skull measuring or measurement of living people, the chemical tests for
determining blood groups, also equated
scales and tables for colour of the eyes,
colour of the hair and colour of the skin.
After the skin colour table of v. Luschan
the geographical distribution of the colour
of peoples' skin is plotted in this world
map (redrawn after Biasutti). The depth of
shades of brown show: the darker the colouring the darker the colour of the skin.

genotypes become, the less they will diverge from one another in type. As ordinates for those, he imagined the compatibility of these genotypes to their momentary environment. From this representation there arose a universal spatial picture of selec-

Fig. 177. Pygmies from the Congo region.

tion. A mountain mass with its peaks is there divided by valleys and saddles. Every possible genotype is designated by a point on the mountain surface, every race occupies a district upon it. Fig. 172 on p 217 illustrates this "spatial scheme of Selection".

A registration of human hereditary characteristics through many generations has hitherto not been possible, one thus could not determine the principle of selection in human propagation communities. Indirectly, suitable hereditary characteristics can, however, be recognised, which may be regarded as a selective adaptation to the conditions of the environment.

The cold and heat forms are striking in man and beast. The light skinned, short, blubber-padded body of the Eskimo and the undersized figure of the Arctic fox with its wide head surrounded by a thick pelt of hair are unequivocal adaptations to an extreme polar climate with constant shortage of nourishment. Such environmental characteristics arose from mutation and selection.

The colour of man's skin is bound by heredity and possesses a high selective value: it is a "mutant" and was "bred" precisely because of its selective advantages. The skin protects man against overheating and being chilled, it also regulates the heat exchange. The skin of negroes is a protection against radiation in a tropical climate. The pigmentation of the skin increases towards the tropics. The lightening of the skin-colour, the depigmentation, results not as an approach to temperate climates, although one must assume that the "white" race is connected with their original environment of the temperate zone. Only when one compares skin colours with the varying strength of the ultra violet rays on earth can it be distinctly seen how climatic factors work selectively on man. It can also be determined how the colour lightening increases with the intensity of ultra-violet light. A fair skin uses the rays to better advantage in a cloudy, misty climate. Tanning or sunburn can protect Europeans in summer against too strong an ultra-violet light — not always since the capacity of the tan to do so varies. Nevertheless, it represents the remainder of an ancient hereditary gene, for the skin of the "whites" was bred in very late and can count as a recent acquisition.

There are thus certain rules of climate, which it is attempted to combine with the selectional value of hereditary characters. Then, however, the boundaries or stages of a climate must synchronise with the steps of hereditary characteristics. On the subject of these "Bergmann, Gloger or Allen" rules, many discussions have flared up amongst scientists. It is, namely, not always possible to arrange the variability of geographical races within such climatic laws. In general the dictum of B. Rensch is valid, who confirmed Bergmann's rule on its selective value: "In the advance of a warm-blooded form into a cooler climate or with the pejoration of the climate of a district the hereditarily larger (in size) variants are preserved to a greater degree, because they can withstand it better owing to a relatively smaller cooling surface." This, Gloger's climatic rule, is especially important: "With a warm-blooded racial circle those races living in warmer, damper regions show a stronger melanine pigmentation than the races in cooler and dryer regions." (Melanines are naturally dark colouring matter which affect the colour of the skin as pigments. The lack of them leads to albinism).

Fig. 178. Semang Negrito shooting an arrow in Malaya. The well proportioned physical growth of this "pygmy" is remarkable.

Here certain necessary remarks are in order: one must guard against over simplifications and the conclusions drawn from them. When the races are divided by the colour of the skin into white, yellow, brown and black, relationships are not al-

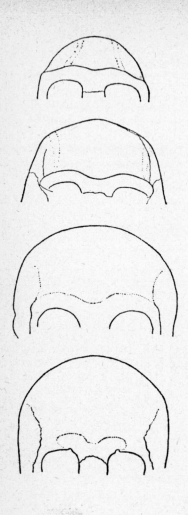

Fig. 179. An evolution of the spirit is intimately bound up with the bodily development of man by Mutation, Selection and Isolation. Spirit, body and soul are inseparable. The illustration shows the increase in the height of the cranium in the course of human racial history. Reading downward: chimpanzee, Sinanthropus, Neandertal Man, and present Man. The physical picture is also a picture of spiritual development (after Weidenreich).

ways necessarily expressed by them. Such intuitive pictures cannot be employed to get correctly the manifold race differentiations. It is quite another thing, as could be followed in Chapter V of this book, when one speaks of the origin of the three racial spheres through Isolation, namely of the great separation in a westerly, easterly and southerly division of mankind. Still less so can one draw negative final conclusions as to the development of the races through the environmental influences of their present habitats. When, for instance, the colour of the skin of a human group does not correspond to the climatic conditions of their present home, one cannot conclude therefrom that man is not subject to climatic influences which are hereditary characteristics. The present habitat of a population has not always been their home, in which they have developed through mutation and selection. When, during the times of the great migrations, a series of human groups travelled immense distances and colonised utterly new regions with quite different climatic conditions, one cannot expect that in this comparitively short time of a few hundreds of years they should have bred to be adapted to their home in exile. When in AD. 428 King Gaiseric led 80,000 Vandals towards North Africa these former inhabitants of Silesia and West Poland had simply not had enough time to acquire a brown skin. The African inhabitants of North America have also hitherto not found it possible to reduce the pigmentation of their skin. There are also races for whom it is quite impossible to adapt themselves to the pigmentation of a new climate; they cannot make certain hereditary characteristics, which they once formed, retrogress. The "whites", that is the extreme North Europoids, simply cannot become darker although originally they came from people with darker skins — they have lost for ever the necessary alleles which they formerly possessed.

When many distinguishable races with different skin colours in Africa live together one must not conclude from that that the tropical climate guide the incomprehensible play of chance in mutations and to drive it in certain directions so that basically not everything behaves in an unruly manner. It will not do even to overestimate the "blind fury" of chance mutations. Man can be changed by mutations only insofar as his genotype permits. Only there in his restricted basic plan does he show a certain readiness to mutate and often only in small qualitative character changes. Mutation could not create horses' hooves out of his feet as, indeed, it also cannot help a horse to become a biped. Colour of hair, colour of eyes, colour of skin, smooth

Homo sapiens
_____

Neandertal man
_____

Sinanthropus
_____

Pithecanthropus
_____

Australopithecine
_____

Anthropoid apes
_____

| 200 | 500 | 1000 | 1500 | 2000 ccm |

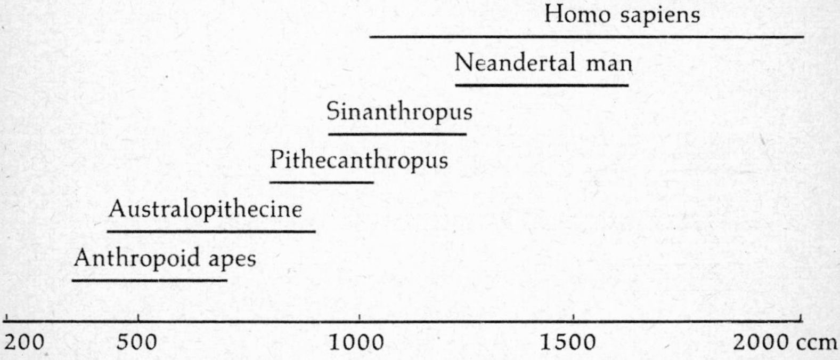

Fig. 180. The development of the volume of the brain (after Schwidetzky and v. Krogh). In the range of variations on the skull capacity, a coherent development becomes apparent which flows slowly onward and does not advance by bounds.

has no influence on their colouring. The Hottentots, with their light skin colour, derive from the comparitively light coloured Hamites. The very dark South African Negroes are probably immigrants from tropical Central Africa.

The selective environment, isolation and pitiless decimation seem to or crinkly or woolly hair are not very deep-going changes, which suffice to over-estimate the value of mutations, especially during the periods of time which we humans can survey.

Not always, however, are such qualitative alterations from the mould of selection dependent on the outer conditions of the habitat. Under

Fig. 181. Picture of a chimpanzee child showing a shattering similarity to a human baby. The adult chimpanzee has lost the candour and the playful curiosity of demeanour of his youth — unspecialized Man preserves these properties during his whole life.

equal climatic conditions and in the same geographical latitude the changes in eye colour, hair colour or size in Europoids and Mongoloids are quite unlike. Here, then, the total of internal inheritance genes is decisive. The means as an entire structure and as the result and end product of a long preceding development can, in this instance, not be altered by outside factors.

This also, however, is not necessarily the rule. Ill-nourished tribal groups who for many generations have dwelt in regions which offer only poor nourishment breed the "small eater". The short stature of the Lapps, North Siberians and Eskimos possesses a selective value.

The "runt" has fewer body cells to feed than the "fat boy".

The tropical and subtropical pygmies of Africa, Asia and the South Seas seem to be an illuminating example of this. According to E. Fischer, who in his opus "On the origin of the pygmies" tried to solve the problem by genetical considerations, this is only *one* cause of the origin of pygmy growth, a modification in a locally isolated group of men who remained small. It seems to show no hereditary shortness and the modified group is said to be no separate race.

According to Fischer, the second cause of the origin of dwarf growth is the following:

"By long selection, lack of food, climatic and other influences, out of a medium- or large-statured population the tall hereditary lines are more and more climinated and finally extirpated. At the same time other special qualities are bred. In this fashion probably originated many pygmoids, the Veddah, for example, the Lapps (?) and others. They represent each a race of its own."

"In the third place dwarf growth occurred in normally growing groups by a jump mutation. The mutation concerned other genes than those involved in the selection process, namely basic growth genes. These mutations were then selected and the

Malaya and Bambuti-Pygmies from the African Ituri Forest. The well proportioned Negritos have nothing in common either physically or spiritually with the Bambuti. But both tribes live in the same environmental conditions, both are nomadic, both settle in blood-related small bands. Semang and Bambuti spend their lives under the same compulsion of nature to breed, and their environment, the primeval forest, is the same. Nevertheless, they differ as much from one another as if they lived in different planets.

Here, perhaps, there arises an imponderable, impenetrable something within a biological human picture

 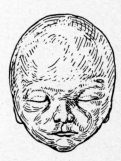

Fig. 182. In human embryonal development the face humanises. The left drawing (after Bromann): foetus in third month, right (after Schultz) foetus in sixth month.

unmutated large specimens extirpated. Simultaneously other qualities mutated and bred on."

This leads to the cultivation of quite distinct forms of small growth. Our illustrations show photographs by the Austrian ethnologist and anthropologist Professor Paul Schebasta. They represent a Semang-Negrito in

which cannot be made plain by causal analysis alone. There are researchers who are openly doubtful. One might put it thus: In the forefront individual facts of the new Darwinian teaching with its development factors, mutation, selection and isolation count heavily in the balance. In a wide review, however,

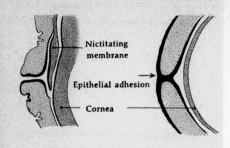

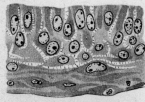

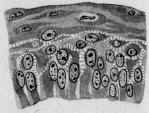

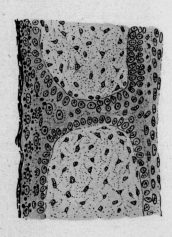

one would prefer to draw nearer to the sense of total human development and to learn to understand it as a whole connected picture. The factors of evolution together with a merely physical-chemical basis of the path of inheritance, which investigates the molecular structure of living matter secreting and atomising and submitting it to a causal analysis — "explains" the human being and life form only on certain intelligible stretches of the way. It often leaves the connecting sense of the whole in the dark. A study of the special case, man, will illuminate the dark through new conceptions of psychology and behaviour research, and might unite spiritual knowledge and natural science.

Here, then, is introduced the idea of the hesitation or slowing down (Retardation) of human development which leads to a rejuvination of the forms. "No other mammal grows at so slow a tempo as man" said L. Bolk, the author of "Das Problem der Menschwerdung" (The problem of the origin of man), "there is none that takes so long to grow up after birth; none with so long a senility" (senium = old age). The domestica-

Fig. 183. The drawings explain some of the processes of the "physiological premature birth" of man which received its explanation through Portmann. The insessorial period of mammals is in man spent in its mothers womb. Eyes and ears are outwardly closed. Above: Eyelid shut in insessorials, left for birds, right for mammals. In the middle, eyelid shut in insessorial birds: the corneas of both eyelids touch closely. Below: eyelid closure in mammal-insessorials: an eyelid adhesion occurs. In man the closure opens in the 5th month.

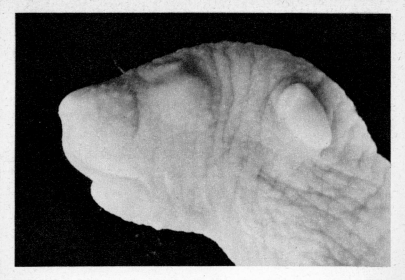

Fig. 184. Mouse on the day of its birth. The eyes are shut fast. The ears which lie forward adhere by the rim.

tion, or better still, selfdomestication of man made changes which first allowed him to become Homo sapiens. One of these presuppositions was the check on development which fixed the youthful characteristics of the wild form and thus the animal predecessors of mankind as lasting characteristics: the curving of the spinal column and the pelvic organs, hair parting, comparitive poverty of pigmentation and finally, as the most important retardation phenomenon, their behaviour. These unspecialized, juvenile characteristics which man shows during his lifetime can be observed in very young, and even foetal, anthropoid apes. The anthropoid ape child is very like the human child. It may also be said that a likeness exists between the genealo-

gically ancient juveniles, and grownups, who in their forms are genealogically more recent. The sense of retardation may lie in that one class of animal, which develops in a differentiated way; becomes "despezialized", rejuvinated — because nature can proceed from these simplified "primitive" characteristics onward to a new specialization.

Formerly a "biogenetic basic law" was believed to be absolutely valid. According to it each individual man passed through, during his embryonal development, every stage of his forebear's development from the worm through the fish to the apes. The history of the development of the individual living being (ontogenesis) was said to be a repetition of the genealogical history. A ple-

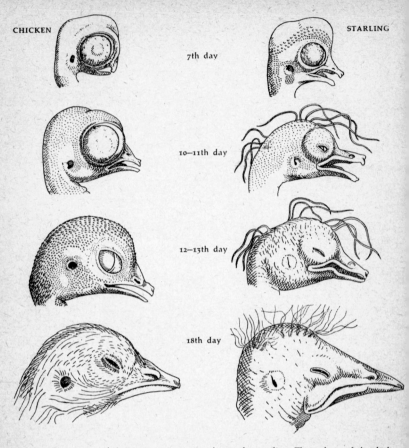

CHICKEN   STARLING

7th day

10—11th day

12—13th day

18th day

Fig. 185. The closing of the sensory organs in a hen and a starling. The embryo of the chick develops without the closing of eye and ear (after Portmann).

thora of convincing facts seemed to support it: the human foetus possesses, up to the third month, a tail, its gill sacs are similar to the breathing organs of fishes. Up to the fourth month the embryo is cloaked in a woolly covering. The metacarpus forms an os centrale (os = bone) such as mammals have but missing in adult man. As Fig. 182 on page 227

shows, the face of the embryo becomes almost human only after six months: the laterally set eyes shift to the front and move together, from the open nostrils the nose is raised up and the snout-like, animal-like countenance becomes the human narrow cleft mouth on which the mucous membranous border of the lips pouts forth.

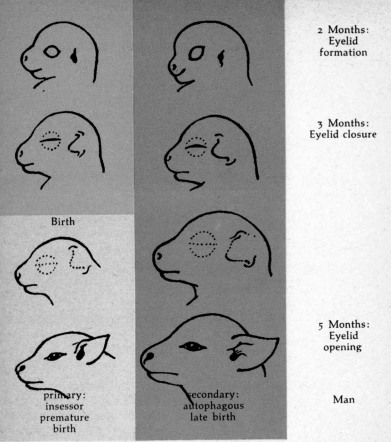

			2 Months: Eyelid formation
			3 Months: Eyelid closure
Birth			
			5 Months: Eyelid opening
primary: insessor premature birth	secondary: autophagous late birth		Man

Fig. 186. Diagrammatic drawing of the closing arrangements of the distant sensory organs in mammals (by Portmann). Here the primary conditions are compared to those of developed groups. Gray colouring shows the uterine phase. The human is however still an embryo in its first year of life (society takes over the role of the uterus) and a "secondary insessor" as a premature birth.

In spite of all these the biogenetic basic law must be severely restricted. The gill sacs do not assert that the human embryo was a fish at that stage, the woolly coat is no proof that at tois stage a monkey has been materialized. In genealogical history only embryos can be compared with embryos never an embryonal figure with a fully grown living being. What is growing in the mother's womb is a human being. This must in ontogenesis first go through the characteristics of the class of animal to which man belongs and thereupon only through the characteristics of his

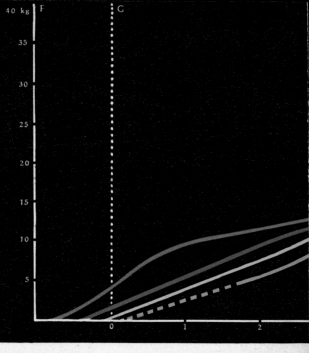

Fig. 187. The human grows quicker than the gorilla, chimpanzee or orang-utan in its first year of life, just as in its embryonic state it increases more rapidly in weight. The special case, man, has a larger head to develop. The greater bodily mass of human sucklings keeps pace with the head growth. It is most unlikely that these circumstances enforce an earlier fruition when the newly born, in the real sense, is not yet "ready". (A = Gorilla, B = Orang, C = Chimpanzee; D = Man; E = years, F = weight, G = birth. Redrawn after Portmann.)

species and race — this intelligence is quite valuable enough.

In embryonic development the figures of the earliest forebears are not repeated. In a rudimentary shape shadows of the immense past arise and vanish again before birth. Do they really disappear? The behaviour of the newborn babe makes one think. The suckling is still guided by the ancient race-historical part of the brain, the basic brain and the spinal cord; the cerebral cortex is not yet sufficiently matured. In his relative helplessness the newborn baby stands rather below a chimpanzee baby. In any event it is not so decided an "insessorial" as sparrows or woodpeckers and its helpless "insessorial" behaviour towards its "artifical" unbiological environment, to which it cannot adapt itself, is relative.

The origin of mankind took place many millions of years ago, by his erecting, freeing of the hands, loss of hair covering, and differentiation of the brain. In the innate behaviour of the suckling nothing can be discovered of this evolution. Its instinc-

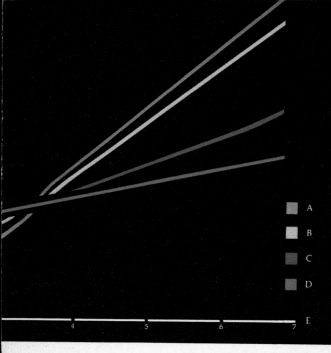

A
B
C
D
E

tive behaviourisms are on a level with the pongids.

A research film by Dr. H. F. R. Prechtel "Reifen der frühkindlichen Motorik" (Maturing of the early infantile motorism) the film which was made with the support of the German research community and in collaboration with the Institute for Scientific films, shows its surviving genealogical and for man now senseless behaviour: The monkeyish grasping reflex for the mother's pelt together with a rythmic breast seeking, the climbing movements, the spinal reflex with the arching of the vertebral column as in tailed amphibians and lizards, the creeping and striding motions and finally even the paddling movements when touched by water. All these "ancestral historical survivals" in the behaviour of the suckling are quenched when the higher parts of the brain mature.

At this point a short review of the intuitive studies and indications of Professor A. Portmann, the Director of the Zoological Institute of the University of Basle, will strengthen the theme. In the realm of birds the concept of animal juvenile development is known, the naked, helpless insessor, and, the self-sufficient chick, the autophagous bird. The groups of birds with a higher organisation have nidicolous (or insessorial) young, those which are lower in the scale, equally less intelligent autophagans (self feeders). In mammals it is the reverse, the less highly organised

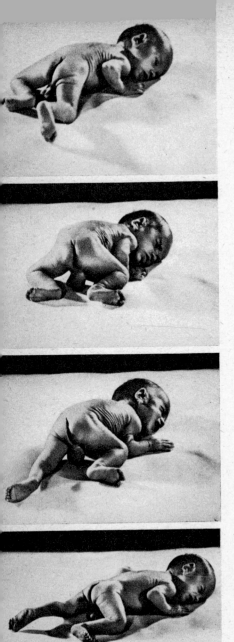

groups bring helpless young into the world, whilst the highly organised mammals with differentiated brain bring "complete" children into the world — autophagous — except man! The, according to his organisation, highest ranking mammal with the highest brain differentiation comes into the world as an insessor. It needs a whole year for him to become autophagous, which the anthropoid apes are at birth.

According to Portmann man distinguishes himself basically in his embryonal development from all the remaining Primates. Were human ontogenesis merely an enhancement of the method of development of the higher mammals then his juvenile condition in the womb would be completely developed only after a period of gestation of one year and nine months, then man also, like all other Primates, would be an autophagous "nest leaver". In that event he would, when newborn, have at his disposal the ability to walk upright and also the preliminary means of communication. In the embryonal condition the human being passes over the stage, typical of nest leavers, of closed sensory organs and arrives in this world with highly developed senses. As a "secondary insessor" he represents, in obeying special laws different from the remaining Primates, a com-

Fig. 188. The creeping movements of a prematurely born child come spontaneously. Walking movements also occur. If a newborn child of a few days is laid on its belly on a firm floor then often creeping movements are made with arms and legs in a trotting movement.

pletely separate species. The long
duration of his growing period —
nearly double that of the pongids —
should not be designated Prolongation or Retardation, according to
Portmann. This concept brings man
inescapably together with the genealogical development which, owing to
his derivation from non humans does
not asses man's value." The astound-
ing new shape of human development is this: The period of gestation
of 20 to 22 months which would be
needed to beget a thorough instinct-
ively determined 'human animal' is
divided into two completely separate
periods; into a uterus period and
into an embryonal first year which
is left to the care of 'society', in which
thus the role of the uterus is taken
over by society. The entire peculiarity
of man, his strong social ties and
traditions, the whole special learning
of his physical attitude as of his
speech but also the power of free
decision are related to this particular form of development. So man
must be conceived as a kind of life
which is formed as a further stage
of development beyond the higher
mammal stage: A' secondary insessor'
with open sensory organs and a particular social articulation."

Even if Portmann does not take a
stand against scientific teaching of
descent, yet according to him the
theories of the origin of man should
not be derived on a basis of fossils,
and the setting up of a universal picture of mankind should not be derived from mammalian physiology.
Typical and characteristic of man is

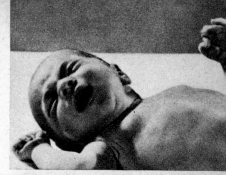
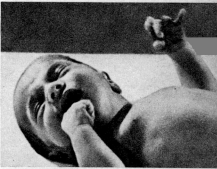
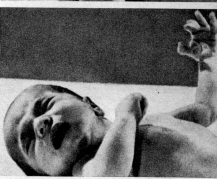

Fig. 189. Prechtl succeeded in 1953 with a
human suckling (an immature prematurely
born one) in observing climbing movements
and filming them. The alternating arm
movements were coupled to the gripping
movements of the hands. The right hand
was carried downwards closed whilst the left
in its upward motion opened more and more.

his social behaviour and only thence
should one appraise and judge. In the

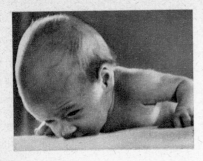

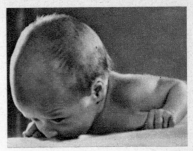

Fig. 190. Cuttings from a strip of the same film represent the "rhythmic breast seeking" as a socalled search automism in an immaturely born child in its second month of life.

social existence form of man there is combined, according to Portmann, the natural biological heir with the spiritual.

This depreciation of evolutionary and genetic research could not fail to be rejected. Man as a "physiological premature birth" was purposeless as an indication of a purely human

Fig. 191. Atavistic traces in the behaviour of the suckling. A series of pictures from a film "Ripening of the early juvenile motorism" (by Prechtl). A finger of the mother touches the palm of the suckling. At once the child's fingers close on this "Impulse body": first middle finger, then ring finger and little finger and finally fore finger and thumb.

specialization which does not contradict a genealogical connection of man with the higher Primates. Even if, according to Raymond Cartier, the diabolical character of science lies in the fact that darkness descends even more thickly upon us by contrast, the more powerfully the light of science shines. And when the same author in face of the incompleteness of fossil finds calls out in resignation: "They have presented us with a thousand uncles but not a single grandfather" — then one should be careful in ones judgment on values. Science which wishes to set up the biological natural history picture of man within its frontiers recognises how often the facts are fragmentary

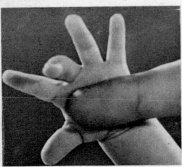

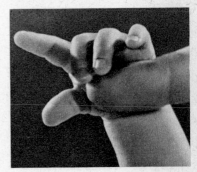

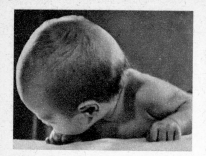 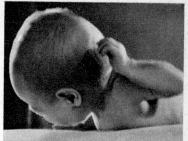

and insufficient. It sees, however, at the same time the whole greatness, depth and coherence of the facts to be deduced from the embryology.

Here we need only to be reminded again, as an extraordinary example, how science conceived a population as a development unit. In the same way it attempts to understand the entire human history from such evolutionary units. This is not a unilateral and not even any longer a purely mechanistically-material task that a structure must unconditionally dissect into portions. It is far from any dogmatism. It demands a selflessness, a prudence and universality of view which pays a high tribute to the courageous dignity of Man — a being, then, who is both object and subject of this investigation.

The true scientist will never forget that he employs only one method, and thus only *one* way among many, in which he tries to understand the world and its contents.

As an investigator on Man he is conscious of the tragic dissension within himself: he must be the living subject of his own scientific activites.

When Linnaeus gave man his generic name Homo he added the words "nosce te ipsum" (Know thyself).

The roads to self-knowledge are many and every man is free to choose his own. He does not diminish the importance of others by doing so.

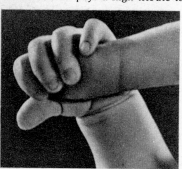 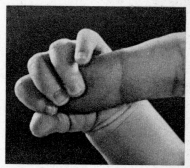

THE FUTURE MAN

When we speak here of a future Man it is not enough to discuss only the fate of humanity during the next hundred or five hundred years. Because man, in common with all living beings, is subject to the constant biological process of gradual change of form and since in the course of his history, and probably today also, very small barely noticeable heritable changes are still taking place, which finally might lead to a change of species. Not even in a thousand or ten thousand years would parts of such processes of change become evident. For the human observer who is restricted to his tiny periods of time the evolution of his own species seems to stand still. We are hardly enabled to re-live three hundred or even three thousand human spans in retrospect, or foretell the processes of our future destiny within twenty thousand or two hundred thousand or more years. The development of Pre-hominines Australopithecus in South Africa to the first emergence of the Aurignacians and Cromagnons lasted about one million years; it thus comprised fifteen thousand human life-spans or thirty to forty thousand generations. In this relatively short period in world history the hominid type submitted to a positively hurricane change of form; indeed he may be looked upon as one af the animal groups whose

potentialities of unfolding with the greatest intensity have been realised. It must, however, by no means be expected that this natural flood of development will dry up with Homo sapiens recens. Man will be unable to remain man as we know him now, a modern sapiens type. He will in the ccurses of the next hundreds of millenia presumably change considerably physiologically and physically. The "only predator within the Primates" —who has been as a hunter of big game not only creator of durable and constant clannish combinations and fighting hordes, but also overcame nature so that he tamed and bred plants and animals — will, in a million years, perhaps be as near or as far from Homo sapiens recens as the Australopithecus is to Homo sapiens. This, of course, presupposes the undisturbed rule of the powers of selection and inheritable mutations, which make possible further evolution without our finished and refined sort of domination and influence on nature.

That is not to say that man is willing to wait patiently until nature with her tremendously slow evolutionary steps leads him upon the way which is profitable for him — or even hurtful — for the forces of selection are incalculable.

Man has long since begun to cultivate himself as he domesticated plants and animals. With transformations and sex determination, artificial insemination, with artificially provoked mutations, with the guiding of the inheritance substances in the germ cells and above all with positive eugenics, man will soon try to outdo his Maker.

There is a widespread idea, especially in circles which are strange or even inimical to natural science, that man as a biological being has now reached the position of an end product. That physiologically and morphologically he is stable and incapable of further development and thus completely out of the reach of natural history. That he has released himself for good from an original spontaneous influence of nature and that his environment will be built up by himself as a self-determined and creative being. With a social conception built up through an international desire man has encroached upon the natural authority of the forces of development — according to his free decision he has himself taken over the role of evolution and therewith has entered into his place having separate laws as a unique phenomenon and as a separate instance of the more or less blind and chancy orbit of natural origins clearly contrasted with all organisms and all higher animals. Hence the future of man would depend on man alone; nature could no longer co-operate decisively in his future destiny.

It was, however, an obvious, essential process of evolution which made it possible for man to "step outside nature"; so to influence blind powers that they carry out services for him. It was the nature and duty of all living beings on this planet for hundreds of millions of years to ensure if possible a favourable position for themselves through unilateral — that is to say one way — adaptations of individual organs in certain directions in a certain environment. This was, and is, the specialization of the various organs in the realms of plants and animals — and every organ could, and can still at some time be, specialised once and irrevocably.

Man also is adapted unilaterally in a quite natural way and one organ proves this specialization: the brain. In man's brain the convolutions and sulci of the cerebral cortex have, as opposed to all other animals and especially the Primates, enormously increased, the microscopic structures are differentiated to the utmost. In particular, certain secondary neopallium regions at the poles and on the inferior side of the frontal and temporal lobes have lately reached so mighty a development that one may very well speak here of a natural specialization — and this unilateral evolution is still in full spate. And precisely the frontal lobe with the Broca 's inferior frontal convolution as a motor centre of speech is, in spite of its development, far from having reached its end.

Here, however, further consideration is necessary: besides the normal unilateral adaptation there exists also a rarer, apparently anomalous "overspecialization". It occurs when organs further unfold even when a favourable condition of adaptation has been exceeded. One knows over-development of incisor teeth of fossil proboscid animals, mastodon and elephas columbi, an overspecialization of the dentition of the sabre tooth tiger, of the horns of the extinct giant deer, quite apart from the ill-shaped and positively fantastic bony growths of the reptiles of the dinosaur period. It is not perhaps quite out of place to consider whether the cortex of our brain also, could not carry out important specializations by an imaginative adaptation—or perhaps has even now reached an over-specialized state. The over-development of teeth, antlers and horns of fossil animals made the original sense of these organs as digging and rooting tools and as weapons against predatory animals, absurd and useless. They bordered on the monstrous and jeopardised the preservation of the species. Even if the word "monstrous" means "contrary to nature" yet such functionless features still do belong to nature.

It may hurt the pride of man if here his brain, as the centre of his spirit, is put in juxtaposition to coarse, bestial, purely mechanical animal organs. Apart altogether that thereby only can the possibility of an over-specialization be brought out, the brain itself and its significance must be evaluated in the right way: the brain directs, guides, controls but it does not perform anything, it does not encourage or drive. It is not the seat of the soul and the spirit; it is a neurocrine organ supplementary to the entire nervous system. An "objective" brain anatomy says nothing at all about our entire physical composition—yet the completeness of man with his capacity for self-knowledge, with his ability to change his environment, with his "region of the roots of feelings and emotions", is governed and controlled by the brain.

Even if we suppose a hypothetical over-specialization of the brain, man has not escaped from nature or even from natural evolution. Brain development very likely will proceed on its way. The fruits of "over cerebration", the over-increased technical-civilized progress are only reflections of our over-developed brain functions. We can govern them just as little as we are able to direct our unilateral or one-way adaptation. If the acquisition of super-dimensional human knowledge destroys us then over-specialization will have done away with our species.

But there is yet another aspect of this hypothetically presumed evolution of the human brain: The over-specialization of the organs of animals, which would otherwise serve for securing food, for defence or attack, have after their over-development no reference at all to physical environment. "These organs have the task of acting purely symbolically, they are there to be seen. They are a catalyst, the reply to questions which occur among neighbouring individuals: in short, for contacts between individuals. The necessary contacts, so far as they occur between members of the same species, are in most instances parts of the functional framework of propagation (that is, the choice of a mate, the care of the brood), the formation of the herd, and preservation of the herd and also all social relations . . . The organs for contacts between individuals are as a rule connected with special movements and ways of behaving of the carrier. They serve to bring to bear the symbolism lying in the shape of the organ, in a suitable way and at the right time." With these words of Dr. W. Schäfer's, has not everything been said which, with the help of an oversized brain, man has realised upon earth and which in the future must continue to drive him onward, without his being able to stop it? The brain which would serve for the ordinary purposes of life and the simple social and spiritual relations of mankind to a sufficient degree now becomes almost exclusively the controller of society. The human brain becomes the symbol of learning and of power and therewith the symbol-carrier immediately gains real power, forces the "formation of a herd", preserves the herd and directs its movements and ways of behaviour.

In such a freely drawn picture there may be a shadowy hint of the truth of how future men will exist. Yet the mighty, peculiarly human and absolutely great development of the frontal portion of the brain permits a quite real survey of the future of man to be taken.

For this one must look closer at the newest investigations of Professor H. Spatz of the Max Planck Institute for Investigating the Brain, which were briefly touched upon in the third chapter of this book, pp. 110/111.

The convolutions of the brain impress themselves upon the inside of the cranium. By taking an impression of the inside of the skull (an endocrane) the outer form of the brain can be more or less reconstructed. Thus, reproductions of a brain which vanished many hundreds of millennia, or even millions of years ago, can often be obtained — if the bony cranium has been preserved. Spatz is of the opinion that the brain shapes its own casing and only t h o s e brain convolutions show themselves on the inner surface of the skull which are, at the moment, in the course of further development; whilst those formed earlier are submerged below the surface. (Internation, in Reman's sense.) When, for instance, in a Chondropterygian the brain does not make any impressions at all on the skull — it is surrounded, namely, on all sides by cerebro-spinal fluid — then, according to Spatz's hypothesis, the development of the brain has in that instance come to a halt. In ungulates or predators, on the other hand, the convolutions have imprinted deep impressions of the dome of the cerebrum in particular on the vault of the cranium: these portions of the brain are thus still engaged in an ontogenetical advance.

This method of investigation now led to astonishing facts: in recent large apes, especially in the gorilla, such impressions are only slightly developed. According to Spatz this is a sign that the brain development of the anthropoid apes has more or less ceased. In present-day man, nevertheless, there are to be seen in the forward and median cranial fossae, deep impressions, namely where the "basal neopallium (convolutions of the inferior surface of the frontal and temporal lobes) lie against the skull, whereas older parts of the brain like the caudex cerebri, the archipallium, the primary neopallium regions and the neopallium in the vault of the cerebrum do not make impressions. In certain fossil Hominoids the convolutions of the basal neopallium were, according to the prints in the skulls which were tested, more lightly developed than in present man whilst in the convolutions of the cerebrum the capability of creating impressions was stronger than in men of our day. According to Chr. v. Krogh the hominoid character of the fossil Hominoids comes out clearly.

For the evolutionary future of living beings investigations are essential which may show how, for parts of the brain which do not unfold until later, room is provided beforehand. Also in the third chapter we have seen that it was in the reptiles that the "neopallium" developed, and was added to the archipallium as a thin layer. Quite late and last in the developments of all living beings there unfolded in Homo sapiens recens the convolutions of the basal cortex in an extremely vigorous manner. By such parts of the brain developing late and strongly, those which developed earlier were submerged ("Internation") by them.

Here are the relations of the function of the brain to its individual parts which are of importance in the course of its ontogenetical development: in the lower vertebrates the archipallium which comprises nearly the entire cerebrum is connected with the sense of smell. In ungulates and predators parts of the cerebral vaulting unfold; those which have to do with movement, hearing, sight and the sense of touch. The fossil Hominid developed the relatively lately obtained regions of the brain in the frontal lobe, the temporal lobe and the parietal lobe which make speech possible. In this connection a remark by Dr. K. Lorenz may be pointed out: "To produce a real tool, perhaps a hand axe" (as opposed to using objects which have been shaped by chance, as a chimpanzee might. Author's note) "an incomparably higher differentiation in duration of memory is necessary through controls of the results of regulated actions. It will seem as if this intimate connection between doing and knowing, between practice and gnosis must presumptively have a special central organ which only man possesses and which is situated in the gyrus supra marginalis of the left inferior temporal brain convolution. If this part of the brain is damaged — in its comprehensive way it also contains the 'centre of speech' in man — in addition to disturbances of speech there are certain lapses in deed as well as of comprehension."

In us present day men the basal neopallium is in the process of development: its bi-lateral destruction leaves hearing, sight, movement, memory and acquired knowledge intact, but social behaviour, the sense of orderliness, the ability to think for oneself and to combat uninhibited impulses are fundamentally injured because they have to do without the control of the brain. "Man is struck to his innermost core, the actually human is taken away from him." (Spatz.) Previously these historically young parts of the brain—and present only in man — were regarded as 'silent' and without importance. By deduction after accidents, brain tumours and lastly through local cerebral atrophy ('Picks disease') which, inter alia, leads to a gradual disappearance of the nerve cells of the basal neopallium, one hoped to disclose the relation of this region of the brain to human intellectual life. With its future increasing development the sides of man which control impulses— so it could be argued—would be widened and strengthened, self control would be improved and his better nature awakened in rich measure. "If we dare to exercise our imagination in order to associate the highest physical attributes, like character and personality, with localisatory presentation, then we will think of an interplay and reciprocity of function of the most recent sections of the neopallium and the same of the ontogenetically old interbrain. To make sense, impulse and judgement must work together harmoniously." (Spatz.) All this does not seem to correspond at all with the assumption of a uni-lateral "cerebration" (development of the brain) of man, among which one understands, after all is said, the specific overriding growth of the pure intellectual capabilities. It is certainly over-rash to subdivide the brain surface as is done at present into individual centres and to limit the functions of the brain by the fixed concepts of an often puerilely conceived psychology. We can thus only perceive at what spot in our body man will in future experience his metamorphoses not, however, how the associations and guiding functions of the brain and of the nervous system will work. The creative performances of man, even of the future man, will not be produced by the brain alone, the whole organism will produce the, as yet, utterly unknown functions of the brain and nervous system. That is why a creative performance cannot be localized in brain centres. Besides the "technical regions of a fairly naïve psychology" like tact, decorum, courtesy, kindness, impulse and uninhibitedness, there are also other driving forces which for the individual may partly replace his own personal peculiarity. In new social orders age-old reactions of man may be altered into world-wide mass psychoses, which remain elementary and natural even if "leading animals" (bell wethers) as the carriers of symbols seem to guide them.

In a lecture Professor A. Remane, reported on his experience in front of an animal's cage in which were chimpanzees from Teneriffe. "Next to me stood one day a woman who obviously saw these creatures for the first time. She gazed at them with eyes staring. Finally she stamped her foot and exclaimed: "It is unheard of that there should be such things." This reaction, an ebullition of temper ("exclamation reaction") which meets the extraordinary with fear and rising hate, especially if it has our own appearance, derives from a biological basic stratum. These elements are taken over, according to Remane, at higher strata and there incorporated in more lofty transactions, the "transports reaction" for instance, in a rite or in a sacrificial ceremony. "Such an over-emphasis by no means always leads the biologically primitive transaction into a higher sphere in the sense of our human ideals. Thus the exclamatory reaction, to continue with the same example, can in the person's own social form become a betrayal reaction during which the greatest barbarity and inhumanity unfolds — the expression bestiality is not apt since the beasts in fact do not know this reaction of betrayal."

Such destinies filled with these or similar mass-reactions can befall man. It can only be safely said that the elementary basic strata out of which human reactions are still being fed after two or three hundred thousand years, cannot be obliterated. Even in a calculable and forseeable social human environment the deepest stratum will throw up the magma of elementary human behaviour as a "euphoria of the outbreak or of the attack" and melt the thin crust of future social orders.

The outer causes are to be sought in the actual pressure of population. It is actual because it can with great probability be foreseen for the next 250 or 500 years — and the future thousand years are pertinent to a survey of future man as a being of human evolution in temporal history. For the year 2050 a world population of 9000 million will have to be reckoned with, in five hundred years with 30,000 million. Seeing that the rate of increase since the birth of Christ was continuous, that the death-rate figures diminished and the birth-rate rose, a sudden cessation of this at least two thousand year old process can hardly be expected. By all estimates the Earth will feed at most ten thousand million people. With the means at the disposal of science it is possible still further to reduce the death-rate and the birth-rate. Hitherto science has steadily reduced the death-rate. "The population-bomb is for mankind an equally dangerous threat as the H-bomb. Luckily its detonation acts more slowly." (R. C. Cook.)

Man practised nuclear fission far too early and equally unprepared will he bring nuclear fusion under control, to produce "Plasma" and to preserve it. Are his genius and his inner composition not up to dealing with these tools? The realities which the physicists brought to life hurriedly, perhaps, precede the realisation of a new being who would be capable of handling them competently.

From all points of view any discussion which has as a theme the fate of the future man must have as a limiting factor the following footnote: thus could a natural or less controlled evolution of Homo sapiens proceed in the course of millennia — if an unforeseen outbreak by atomic, bacterial and chemical Powers does not prepare, in the form of nerve poisons, a senseless blind ending to a sensible development. This, however, adds an uncertain factor to an already problematical investigation, which puts a doubtful colour on all hypotheses for the future. Should the too hastily created powers slip out of the control of man, then it could instantly interrupt not only the evolution of mankind but also that of all higher organised living beings. At the very least the survivors would withdraw from the habitats disturbed so chaotically or by the increase of mutations threatening to life, lose all chance of a future.

These final remarks, as well as the contents of the entire book, should not go beyond the borders of biological natural-history, the imaginary picture of man in terms of the mundane-temporal should not simultaneously overflow on to a metaphysical plane of the timeless-infinite. Making sense of the seemingly senseless course of natural-history should not diminish the importance of natural laws.

They are limited but they yet manifest o n e form of phenomenon: the Powers have implanted in us a sense of orderly respect for the law.

My sincerest thanks are due to the following Personalities for reviewing my manuscripts and for their kind assistance.

Professor Gerhard Heberer of the Anthropological Institute of the University of Göttingen, Professor Wilhelm Gieseler of the Anthropological Institute of the University of Tübingen, Professor H. Spatz of the Max-Planck Institute for Brain research of Giessen, Drs. Johannes Hürzeler and Hans E. Schaefer-Hoch of the Natural History Museum in Basle, Dr. Klaus Doderer of the Paedagogical Institute Schloss Heiligenberg in Jugenheim near Darmstadt, Dr. Reimut Wette of the Zoological Institute of the University of Heidelberg for his collaboration in the part of the sixth chapter on the genetics of heredity, for which he not only provided illustrations but also made some personal sketches.

For advice and provision of material for illustrations I am deeply indebted to:

Professor I. Schwidetzky of the Anthropological Institute of the University of Mainz, Dr. O. Schuster of the Senckenbergische Naturforschende Gesellschaft in Frankfurt on Main, Professor Adolf Portmann of the Zoological Institute of the University, Basle, Dr. H. E. R. Prechtl, Algemeen Provinciaal-Stads en Academisch Ziekenhuis, Groningen, the Chicago Natural History Museum and the Geochronometric Laboratory of Yale University in New Haven, Connecticut, USA.

Mr. Friedrich Grieger, Librarian in Baden-Baden has my heartiest thanks for the provision of a great variety of literature.

Gustav Schenk, Ebersteinburg über Baden-Baden, June 1961

INDEX OF TECHNICAL TERMS

INDEX OF NAMES

LIST OF ILLUSTRATIONS AND TABLES

BIBLIOGRAPHY

COLE, SONIA	The prehistory of East Africa, Penguin books, London
DARWIN, C.	Collected Works, 1875–1888
HOOTON, E.	Up from the Ape, New York 1947
HUXLEY, J.	Man in the Modern World, London 1947 and others
LEAKEY, L. S. B.	Adam's Ancestors, London 1953
LE GROS CLARKE,	History of the Primates 1960
Sir W. E.	British Museum (Nat. Hist.)
OAKLEY, K. P.	Man the Toolmaker 1957
	British Museum (Nat. Hist.)
SIMPSON, G. G.	The Principles of Classification and a Classification of Mammals, Bulletin, American Museeum Natural History 85; New York 1945
WEIDENREICH, H.	Apes, Giants and Man, Chicago 1946
WOOD-JONES, F.	The Principles of Anatomy as seen by The Hand, London 1944.

ACKNOWLEDGEMENTS OF SOURCES

(Notices of scientific copyright will be found occasionally in the vicinity of the relevant illustrations).
The graphic form of the drawings, redrawings, tables and illustrations were provided by Bernd Fahrenholz denoted by an F.

Title page phot. Ittenbach, Berlin
Fig. 1   phot. Marburg and F.
Fig. 2   From "Triangel" Sandoz periodical for medicinal science Vol. 4, No. 5, 1960
Fig. 3   phot. DES Bantlet-Armand Denis productions
Fig. 4   F. after Schenk
Fig. 5   Zoological Inst. Kiel
Fig. 6, 7 F.
Fig. 8   F.
Fig. 9   F. after Schenk
Fig. 13   F.
Fig. 15   phot. Senckenberg Nat. Hist. Society, Frankfurt
Fig. 16   F. relying on publications from Barnett: "Die Welt, in der wir leben", Munich 1957
Fig. 17   F. after Schenk
Fig. 18   From "Die Umschau" 1954/19
Fig. 19   phot. Cy La Tour, N. York
Fig. 20   phot. Popper, London
Fig. 21   F.
Fig. 22   F. after publications by Huxley: The story of evolution, London 1958, Rathbone Books Ltd.
Fig. 23   F.

Fig. 24, 25 phot. Animal picture archives Okapia, Frankfurt
Fig. 26   F. after Schenk
Fig. 27   F.
Fig. 28   F. after Schenk
Fig. 30   phot. British Museum (Nat. Hist. London)
Fig. 31   From "Triangel" Sandoz periodical for medicinal science Vol. 4, No. 5, 1960
Fig. 32, 33 F.
Fig. 34, 35 From a contribution by K. Knußmann in the "Umschau" 1959/22
Fig. 38   F. after Schenk
Fig. 40   F.
Fig. 41   F. after Schenk
Fig. 42   phot. Geochronometric Laboratory of Yale University U. S. A.
Fig. 43   phot. Schumann, Munich
Fig. 44   From Westermanns Atlas for World History, Brunswick 1956
Fig. 45   Schenk
Fig. 46   From "China im Bild" (China in pictures) 1958, 1
Fig. 49   Heberers archives
Fig. 50   B, C: Archives of Koenigswald
Fig. 51, 52 From: W. Gieseler "Fossilgeschichte des Menschen" (Fossil history of man) Stuttgart, 1959. Publ. G. Fischer
Fig. 54 B phot. Ullstein Picture archives, Berlin
Fig. 57   Schenk

Fig. 59   Archive of the Anthropological
          Inst. Tübingen
Fig. 60   F. after Schenk
Fig. 61   Archive of the Anthropological
          Inst. Tübingen
Fig. 62   F.
Fig. 63   Nat. Hist. Museum, Chicago
Fig. 65   F.
Fig. 66   phot. Solecki
Fig. 67   From T. D. Stewart "The restored
          Shanidar skull" Washington, 1959,
          Smithsonian Institution
Fig. 68   F.
Fig. 71, 72 F, 73 From "Man in space and
          time with particular reference to
          the Oreopithecus problem". Nat.
          Hist. Museum, Basle.
Fig. 74   F after Schenk whilst using a map
          by Geographical Projects, London
Fig. 78   From "The large Brockhaus"
          16th Edn. Wiesbaden, 1955
Fig. 79   F.
Fig. 80   F. after an article out of "Brock-
          haus" 16th Edn.
Fig. 84, 85 From a contribution by H. Spatz
          "Thoughts upon the future of man's
          brain and the idea of supermen"
          in "The Super Man" (Der Über-
          mensch) published by E. Benz,
          Zürich, 1961
Fig. 87   phot. Archive Anthropological Inst.
          Tübingen
Fig. 88   phot. Ullstein Picture archives,
          Berlin
Fig. 89   F.
Fig. 90   phot. Ullstein Picture archives,
          Berlin
Fig. 91   phot. Monaco Museum of
          Prehistoric Anthropology
Fig. 94   F. after various publications
Fig. 95   phot. Nat. Hist. Museum, Vienna
Fig. 96   phot. Museo Nazionale L. Pigorini,
          Rome
Fig. 97   phot. Musée de l'Homme, Paris
Fig. 98   From "Orion" Munich, 1958/5
Fig. 99   Contributions Zotz, Inst. for
          Prehistory, Erlangen
Fig. 100 phot. Moravian National Mus.
          Brno
Fig. 102—104 From Gieseler "Descent and
          racial information of Man"
          Oehringen 1956. Publ. by Hohen-
          lohes bookshop
Fig. 105 F.
Fig. 106, 107, 110, 111, 112, ʃ11 'ʃ11
          From P. Graziosi "The art of the
          Palaeolithic Era", Stuttgart
Fig. 108 phot. Dietrich, Ebersteinburg
Fig. 114 phot. Ed. Mazenod, Paris
Fig. 116 Dietrich, Ebersteinburg

Fig. 117 phot. Ed. Mazenod, Paris
Fig. 118 phot. Ed. Mazenod, Paris
Fig. 119 phot. Dietrich, Ebersteinburg
Fig. 120 phot. Ed. Mazenod, Paris
Fig. 121 phot. Frobenius Inst.
          Frankfurt on M.
Fig. 122 phot. Ed. Mazenod, Paris
Fig. 124 F. 125, 126, 127, 128, 129, 230
          from H. Lhote "The rock paintings
          of the Sahara" Würzburg 1958.
          Pub. by A. Zettner
Fig. 132 F.
Fig. 134 From a contribution by H. Petri in
          "Die Umschau" Frankfurt, 1957/3
Fig. 135 phot. Frobenius Inst.
          Frankfurt on M.
Fig. 136 phot. Ullstein Picture archives
Fig. 137 Picture archives South German
          Publication
Fig. 138, 139 F.
Fig. 140 phot. Archiv of the Lindenmuseum,
          Stuttgart
Fig. 141 F.
Fig. 142 From Schwidetzki "Das Menschen-
          bild der Biologie" (The human
          picture of biology)
          Publ. G. Fischer, Stuttgart
Fig. 144, 147, 150 F.
Fig. 145 A, D, from v. Eicksted "Die For-
          schung am Menschen" (Research
          on man) Stuttgart 1957, Publ. Enke
          B, C, F phot. Ullstein Picture
          archives. E from Wastl "Basch-
          kiren" Vienna 1958. Anthropo-
          logical Society of Vienna.
Fig. 146 A phot. Bildarchiv South German
          Publ. B & C from v. Eickstedt
          "Die Forschung am Menschen"
          Stuttgart 1957 Enke Publns. D, E
          phot. Ullstein Picture Bildarchiv,
          F from Weninger "West African
          Negroes" Vienna Anthropological
          Society
Fig. 148 A, B, C phot. Ullstein Picture
          Archives. D, E, F from v. Eicksted
          "Die Forschung am Menschen"
Fig. 149 A, B, C phot. Ullstein Picture
          Archives
Fig. 151 A, B, C phot. Ullstein Picture
          Archives
Fig. 152 phot. Archiv of the Inst. für Aus-
          landsbeziehungen, Stuttgart
Fig. 153 phot. Ullstein Picture Archives
Fig. 154 F.
Fig. 155 From Schwidetzki "Das Menschen-
          bild" (The human picture)
Fig. 156 phot. Wette
Fig. 157 F.
Fig. 158 phot. Wette
Fig. 159, 160, 161 F.